AFFORDABLE PASSIVE SOLAR HOMES
Low-Cost, Compact Designs

by
Richard L. Crowther
FAIA

SciTech Publishing Company
Denver, Colorado

Prologue

This book is for the potential home owner with a frugal budget; a builder or developer seeking affordable, compact, market-responsive homes; the architect and solar designer seeking low-cost, easy to build, livable, energy-efficient designs; the instructor and student looking for conceptual practicalities; interior designers wanting a guideline to passive solar; individuals and firms engaged with equity financing; and, realtors who are stimulated by new land-use potentials.

These passive solar home plans and designs range from compact, midsized, and multiple to ultracompact and survival concepts. They are affordable in initial cost with minimal demand on materials, labor, and construction time, and also offer affordable life-cycle costs.

These designs lend themselves well to independent, attached, in-fill, or add-on living units as well as studios, guest houses, resort units, second homes, motel units, military and civilian housing, elderly and medical living quarters, and for small-scale solar communities.

They are ideally suited for protective shelter or as replacement housing in the event of a disaster.

Library of Congress Cataloging in Publication Data

Crowther, Richard L.
   Affordable passive solar homes.

   Bibliography: p.
   1. Solar houses — Design and construction. 2. Solar energy — Passive systems. I. Title.
TH7414.C77 1984   728'.69   84-5404
ISBN 0-916653-00-5

Printed in the U.S.A.

Published by:
   SciTech Publishing Company, Inc.
   P.O. Box 587
   930 S. Monaco Parkway
   Denver, Colorado 80224

Contents

Chapter 6. Interiors

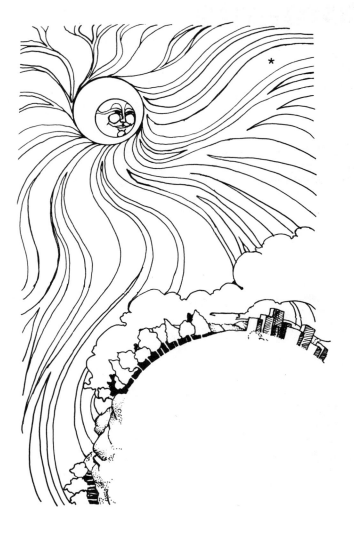

Chapter 7. Conclusion

Part 2. Home Designs — Floor Plans and Characteristics

Appendixes

References

Glossary

Foreword

The affordability of a home rests upon many factors. A particular advantage of a new passive solar home is reduced dependence upon conventional energy sources throughout the lifetime of the building. Small homes especially lend themselves well to passive solar design. Cost-effective direct gain systems such as sunspaces can be used to receive and retain solar-thermal energy and reduce heat losses from interior livable spaces. Sunspaces, featured in many of the designs in this book, allow for supplementary and overflow space uses and can also serve a greenhouse function.

The designs presented in this book are conceptual, intended to serve as an aid to the potential home owner, or to developers, contractors, solar designers, architects, engineers, or interior designers. *The passive solar designs shown primarily emphasize solutions for cold-climate and temperate zones of the United States, within the principal need for passive solar systems.*

Merely shrinking the size of a space within a home to achieve affordability is not enough. Every facet should be examined to substantially increase the economic opportunities for home ownership. These facets include an affordable way of life, affordable financing, demographic and climatic factors, affordable site, affordable architecture, minimizing mechanical demand, and providing an affordable interior.

Building a new home is a complex but rewarding experience. Many intimate and critical decisions have to be made. It leads to an introspection of ourselves, our families, and our relationships with our loved ones and friends. Custom building by ourselves or with a contractor forces the acceptance or rejection of innumerable options with long-term effects upon our finances and way of life.

Buying an already-built home is a less intense experience. However, without the deeper involvement that comes from building a house, we can be beguiled by superficialities, nostalgic conventions, and eye-catching effects rather than focusing on designs that fundamentally optimize long-term benefits. Other negative aspects can be improper orientation; obstructions to solar use; disregard for climatic planning; meaningless architectural form; lack of effective thermal mass; lack of solar and natural heating, cooling, and ventilating systems; disregard for the energy properties of color, texture, and material; thermal bridging; inadequate insulation; excessive infiltration; and traditional fireplaces that can escalate a lifetime of energy costs.

Unfortunately, with either custom or already-built homes, the builder's or home owner's preconceived notions of architectural style and design concepts can stand in the way of commonsense, energy-conserving housing design.

This book examines achieving an affordable home by cost-conscious energy design. The designs and plans of this book present total, integrative, energy design. They carefully integrate site, architecture, and interior for various population segments that meet a frugal budget. Affordable, compact, and energy-efficient homes should optimize the use of sun, air, earth, and water energies; optimize human vitality; reduce stress; and expand opportunities for human enjoyment and creativity.

The book is divided into two sections. The first part gives data concerning design, construction, site, climatic factors, materials, interiors, financing, and other home ownership factors that enhance affordability. Basic information on the design assumptions and considerations incorporated into the homes is presented, along with passive solar systems descriptions. The second part presents designs and plans with a brief review of considerations that serve defined human living needs, as well single-family, attached, or multiple residential configurations. The plans are based on a dimensional grid using 4-foot and 2-foot (1.2 meter and .61 meter) increments compatible with economic standard lumber and materials sizes.

About the Author

Richard L. Crowther, FAIA, has been honored nationally and internationally for his research, innovation, solar pioneering, and energy-efficient design for homes and buildings. His concepts focus on livability, human well-being, energy saving, and disciplined cost.

Crowther's work dates back to low-cost housing built prior to World War II; modular construction during the 1940s; a passive solar home in California in 1945; subsequent energy-efficient residential and commercial architectural projects in more than 30 states, Mexico, and Canada; and a continuance of passive, hybrid, and active solar design through 1985.

He has been an instructor, competition judge, lecturer, or advisor at major universities, the Smithsonian Institution, International Solar Energy Society, Solar Energy Research Institute, and the American Institute of Architects. He has chaired numerous committees on energy, design, research, education, and planning.

Crowther's book *Sun/Earth* (in its fourth edition, Van Nostrand Reinhold) covers the optimized design of sun, earth, wind, and water energies for homes and buildings. It is an ideal companion to this book, *Affordable Passive Solar Homes.*

Crowther's architectural work is extensively published in leading journals, books, and magazines in the United States and abroad.

Acknowledgments

Appreciation is gratefully given to: Robert F. Steimle for evaluation and editing; Douglas Rosendale for delineation assistance; John D. Anderson, FAIA, for reviewing the manuscripts and drawings and providing constructive criticism; American Solar Energy Society for anonymous peer review by one of its members.

Special Credits

Architectural plans, designs and illustrations by the author.

Part 1

Affordable Passive Solar Design Considerations

Introduction to Part 1

Affordable housing has become a fading dream. Now, more than ever, people need the emotional security that a home provides. Most people desire their own home. In a world of uncertainties, conflict, and violence, the home is the last refuge of human emotions, personal identity, and possessions. "Affordable" means not only the ability to make a down payment and carry a mortgage but also to afford all of the other costs associated with home ownership, such as taxes, insurance, maintenance, repair, landscaping, utilities, and transportation to schools, stores, offices, and recreational, medical or other places. It is to have a balanced, affordable way of life. Thus, personal habits, needs, and desires dictate to a large extent the ability to pay not only for the mortgage but ever-escalating utility bills, healthful food, medical needs, education, recreation, entertainment, art, music, crafts, other hobbies, property, possessions, and clothing. A self-sustaining life-style is based on low-cost demands. Growing your own organic food; avoiding expensive (and usually less nourishing) convenience foods, disposables, and energy-wasting products; making only essential use of a car and walking, bicycling, or using the telephone in place of driving; turning off the lights; using waste as a resource; doing things at home; practicing prevention; and, doing your own maintenance and repair is the road to affordability.

Now, with mounting stress, tension, uncertainty, and unrest, we are in a period adverse to home ownership. Financing, inflation, land, construction materials, labor, and utility costs are discourgingly high. If adversity is the best teacher, the time is ripe to change living concepts, means, and methods. Our disposable society transforms simple needs into spectacular wastefulness. Shelter reaches grandiose proportions of misdirection. Food, with nutrients extracted, is disguised by inorganic chemicals and flushed with artificial color and flavor.

Energy-intensive and wasteful habits dilute our ability to buy or build a new home. Our energy-use habits leave trails of air pollution to and from site and architecture, businesses, shops, schools, theaters, restaurants, galleries, medical facilities, and other places. An affordable life-style should replace our wasteful habits with a focus on health and creativity. In seeking value systems, the first question to ask is what people want of themselves. Everyone needs self-esteem. Everyone wants to find meaning in life. Everyone wants an opportunity for personal expression. Home food production in greenhouses and gardens, home recreation and entertainment, and energy and water conservation are all part of an affordable way of life. Affordability is essentially a personal matter.

Affordable homes can fit changing patterns of human life. A well-planned, modest-cost, passive energy home can adapt to long-term changing space needs. In the interest of having a home, people, too, can adapt to a compact housing scale.

Compact homes are not a new phenomenon. Homes of the past were often small, with single baths and rudimentary kitchens. In many communities homes were less than 1,200 square feet (111.5 square meters) with two and three bedrooms. Electrical wiring was minimal, convenience outlets were few, and most homes had only a central ceiling light. A 110-volt, 60-amp fuse served an entire single-family home. Gravity-flow, air-ducted furnaces operated on coal and oil. People managed to live, survive and raise families in these fundamental, compact dwellings.

This book presents compact, livable designs that optimize space planning and the use of passive solar energy, providing an affordable home without sacrificing comfort.

The Matter of Luxury

Luxury in dwellings is usually equated with extra bathrooms, spacious rooms, elevated ceilings, fireplaces, and a host of minor features calculated to beguile the potential home owner. The intent of the presented plans and designs is to devise sensible, efficient, livable concepts with frugal use of materials and labor. The feeling of interior space has been expanded by open planning; floor-to-ceiling glazing that usually brings the landscape indoors; light, reflective colors; the absence of unnecessary detail; and, relatively clean design lines. These qualities impart a sense of true luxury rather than conventional, superficial, "luxury" sales features.

There is little argument that efficient, well-appointed kitchens, extra bathrooms, and interior space openess are desirable, but the real need for many persons is to provide an affordable habitat. Is it logical to channel the construction budget into superficial luxuries or toward fundamental needs? Furthermore, luxury is a matter of quality design in furniture and furnishings, exterior landscaping, and interior surface treatments. The concept of luxury rests largely within

the mind and within the relative quality and design of the total relationship of architecture, its site, and its interior.

Compact living has to be a state of mind as well as a physical reality. Affordability is also a state of mind. Affordable, compact, basic living is one reality and affordable luxury is another.

From the basic conceptual plans presented, it is possible to uniformly enlarge any compact plan or various parts thereof. It is also possible to add luxury features in any measure that a budget may allow. The decision always has to be made between providing the needed basics for living versus less cost-effective luxuries. Unfortunately, too many of today's considered "basics" were luxuries of the recent past.

In review, many luxuries can be added some time after the completion of construction, whereas space cannot be economically expanded. Simply put, it's better to buy cost-effective space than cost-intensive luxuries.

Home Ownership Economics

One of the major costs of home owner-

ship is land. In 1980, land cost made up 23 percent of the price of an average, single-family home, according to the National Association of Home Builders.[1] With land costs come associated development costs for curbs, gutters, sewers, utilities, and access to streets. It is not unusual to find site costs in the best neighborhoods to be 25 to 50 percent of the projected construction cost of a home. High-density land-use patterns that permit zero-property-line construction or other regulatory relief are needed to make affordable, urban homes possible.

Major problems in land use are zoning regulations that, on the one hand, require open space for light and air but, on the other hand, place serious constraints on unobstructed solar access. As human density increases and sites become smaller, careful, interrelated solar access planning becomes critical. Obstructive landscaping or shading by neighboring buildings should be limited by regulations of the developer, city, county, or state. Space on the site for gardening, landscaping, outdoor living, and recreation can be increased by under-

[1]Bruce Stokes, "Housing: The Environmental Issues," *Sierra,* vol. 67, no. 5, Sept./Oct. 1982, p. 45.

ground housing and the use of roofs for such purposes. Keeping the "footprint" (land coverage) of the architecture as small as possible conserves land and construction. The same amount of interior square footage incorporated into more-than-one story can result in more effective land use.

The location of the home on the site, its orientation, height, roof lines, and physical volume affect its immediate neighbor to the north in regard to the seasonal sun path. Homes located further northward have to be further apart to receive the same degree of solar exposure. The colder the climate, the more important it is to reduce utility-energy demand by optimizing on-site solar radiation and earth properties. Not to use solar or other passive energies or employ a total range of conservation measures that can have selective payback periods of three to seven years is to waste money. Savings of 30 to 100 percent on seasonal heating, cooling, and ventilating costs, depending on the regional climate, microclimate, and design solutions, can be realized at a zero-to-seven-percent increase in initial costs.

Besides the benefit of an equity gain likely to increase with time, side benefits of home ownership can be a big help to the budget. Business functions performed at home can be a source of primary or supplemental income.

A basic problem in custom design is that desires usually exceed needs and budget limitations, especially with larger homes. It is important that the custom home owner be well versed in costs and alternative economic options. A holistic-economic, energy-conscious approach is essential for the home building budget to be wisely and effectively prioritized. Every dollar must be carefully weighed and selectively channeled into the most appropriate slot of architecture, landscaping, or the interior. The choices among many complex external and internal architectural options can be confusing; however, by categorizing the options and establishing the accompanying direct and indirect costs, cost-benefit priorities can be established. Comparative desirability of options, along with operational, maintenance, and replacement costs, should be included in the analysis.

Design remains the ultimate determinant of initial and ongoing costs. Affordability is specific to each person and project. All of the direct and indirect factors should be measured within total costs. Unmeasurable, unforeseen factors and emergency circumstances can mess up any well-planned budget. However, not to let this discussion end on a negative note: To build, participate in, or even to watch all of the construction processes involved in creating a new home is a memorable reflection of ourselves, our wants, and our desires taking form. It is an expression with which we can identify and that identifies us.

Affordable Financing

In custom home construction, the services of an architect or home designer, a survey, a soils test, taxes, and the cost of the site itself usually have to be cleared before a construction and mortgage loan commitment is granted. Many people may not be aware that both construction financing and mortgage financing are usually needed to build and purchase a home. The intent of this book is to provide basic concept plans so that probable costs can be estimated by a general contractor, whether for an assemblage of subcontractors or for complete construction services. If you use the general contractor for estimating only and not construction, he/she should be reimbursed for his/her time.

A stickier problem is obtaining satisfactory construction and mortgage finance loans. The procedure is to check with various banks or savings and loan associations and shop around for mortgage money. Beware of adjustable-rate loans unless they are at time-established rates that you feel are acceptable. Some savings and loan institutions have added provisions such as interest-rate ceilings that give home buyers a degree of protection when interest rates rise. Combining your loans with those of another owner of your attached duplex or multiple unit may be a help. Some contractors and developers have packaged loan services. Some framing companies will underwrite the construction loan period. All loans require interest and, generally, mortgage-loan finance percentage points up front. Life insurance can be used as a source for borrowing money, often at a lower interest rate. Also, some city and county governments may have special bond money or other funding available for home loan borrowers.

Banks and savings and loan associations could spread their risk by dividing up their loan commitments among a greater number of small land and housing units. Loans that adjust to interest-rate fluctuations can imperil the home buyer. Long-term, fixed-interest-rate loans can be unfair to the lender. A closer examination is needed relative to the money supply, inflationary interest rates, and how marketable your home is likely to be. The answer is to develop a balanced value dynamic that allows the home owner to ride out difficult economic times but gives the mortgage agency security and not less than an equitable interest return for a temporary period. Mortgage companies and other lenders should look closely at the life-cycle energy-cost advantages of well-designed and well-constructed passive solar homes, with a commitment to smaller site sizes and architecture. Affordable, energy-conserving homes that save on utility costs and contain less equipment to repair or service can allow the home owner to better meet the schedule of mortgage payments.

Short-term mortgages are becoming available for persons with greater initial down payments or who can make higher mortgage payments. The myriad of home mortgage, financial packages that realtors, developers, and lenders are offering can be very confusing. Be sure of exactly what your obligations are under the terms of the agreement. Watch out for discretionary clauses that allow loan readjustments without requiring that the home buyer be notified in advance. Home loan financing should be approached with caution, since, for many people, attractive and affordable financing can make the difference between renting or buying.

Design and Construction

Home design and construction around the world vary according to need, desire, concept, means, and methods. The availability of suitable materials, the manual or technological building methods, and influences of culture and life-style result in a great vocabulary of architectural types and forms. The size, form, proportion, and site relationships of housing units to each other and to the earth can produce a textural habitat that responds more or less favorably to the earth, the atmosphere, the vegetation, and the climate.

Sun, earth, air, and water energies together with cultural acceptance of architectural forms should structure our design concepts. Unfortunately, in energy terms, we have seldom used design and construction to optimize the use of natural, on-site energies.

The new, updated, 1983 edition of *Sun/Earth* (Van Nostrand Reinhold, publisher) by the author addresses these fundamental concepts, effective energy alternatives, and the importance of total, integrative energy design. Sometimes it is more effective and economic to plant a few large trees than to provide architectural shading by overhangs and other devices. Sometimes it is better to arrange interior furniture for thermal comfort than to expend the cost and effort of an architectural solution. Design and construction is fraught with an endless sea of options. *Sun/Earth* has a holistic, energy design process chart that dwells on human, site-development, architectural, and interior design strategies to help prioritize and understand the interrelationship of numerous design options and choices.

Unless someday it may be airborne, all architecture starts with a foundation that is supported by the earth or by a body of water (that rests on the earth). The surface and substrate composition of the earth varies greatly from place to place. Soils tests and soils analyses, where available, or the practical experiences of people who engineer or build in an area are important to the foundation and construction of a home. Surveys are important to determine the location and topographic siting of a residence along with vehicular access and surface drainage.

Every site is unique with its own characteristics and its own microclimate. Every site is a solar collector, as is the architecture, with its interior and its inhabitants. Since the sun literally falls on most doorsteps, the question is how to make the best use of solar energy for heating, air tempering, humidification, dehumidification, and

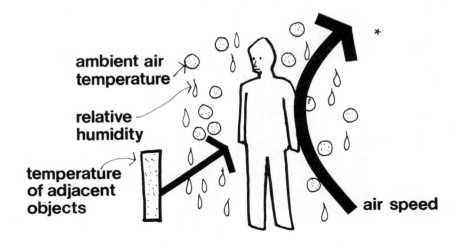

ambient air temperature

relative humidity

temperature of adjacent objects

air speed

cooling homes for human comfort. Comfort, however, cannot be directly equated with human vitality and state of health. Human bodies perform best with some moderate levels of stress. The metabolic and psycho-neural systems of our bodies (including our minds) are exercised by variety and change. Comfort is individualistic. We all respond differently to temperature, humidity, and air movement. Our own bodies' internal fluctuations and sensory perceptions influence our responses to environmental stimuli. A home is not just a shelter from the climate or for privacy or physical protection, but it is an earth-, climate-, and human-response mechanism. Thus, every home — or the same design and construction of a home built on another site — has its own patterns of comfort, energy-effectiveness, and aesthetic attributes. The architect, designer, home owner, and builder or developer should all be sensitive to the human factors as well as the daily and seasonal climatic aspects of the site.

Design should never be taken too lightly. Whatever we plan, design, and build stays with us inevitably for the length of our occupancy of a home and its site. Compact homes in particular, while providing economic and energy values, restrict space and movement. Livability was a key concern of the conceptual plans developed for this book.

How much a person can adapt to some of these very small and even ultracompact designs remains a personal question. The absence of some amenities, such as linen closets, pantries, garden-tool storage, or just storage, may be more than some individuals can bear. In any case, the plans and designs presented are only conceptual and the same plan and elevation (in most cases) can be expanded without too much modification. Another answer is simply to shift to a larger home model that is still relatively compact for what it has to offer. The addition of a garage, a freestanding storage shed (an appendage should match the architecture), or, in some cases, a roof change that allows for a usable attic (pull-down ladders can always be installed) can alleviate both storage needs and human anxiety.

Personal security can be another major design factor. The lack of attached garages with automatic garage door openers can jeopardize physical safety in urban or other areas. All design should be measured not only in cost and energy but also in the reality of human protection and survival.

Although a number of the plans and designs require an absolute minimal amount of material, labor, or knowledge to construct, some problems are bound to ensue and, in any case, someome experienced with construction should guide the work. All the plans have been laid out to a 4-foot (1.2 meter) module to avoid waste and to use standard-sized materials most effectively. Additions or plan expansions should be kept to the same module for economy and ease in building.

Traditionally, architects have not been employed to build individual moderate- and low-income homes. The field of the architect has largely been for upper-crust custom homes and forms of condominium and multifamily living. The advent and growing consciousness of solar design has greatly enhanced the opportunity to custom design or offer housing prototypes that would serve a greater cross section of individual housing needs.

Even though the economics for the architect and home designer are more marginal for moderately low to low-cost housing, the chance to be effective in design and cost remains. This book, with its conceptual, minimal material, minimal labor, optimally cost-effective solar and conservation plan and design outlook, offers a particular opportunity for the architect, designer, builder, contractor, and home owner to avoid having to start from scratch.

To orient the reader to the design concepts integrated into this book, the following is a summary of the principal factors used in the design of these afforadable, passive solar homes:

- economic passive solar design
- optimal livability in minimal space
- optimum flexibility in use
- natural inductive ventilation and cooling; effective cross ventilation
- climatic interior thermal zoning; optimized year-round thermal comfort
- effective daylighting
- minimal site-size requirement and on-site construction layout
- greenhouse gardening
- use of standard, off-the-shelf construction materials
- minimal materials needed to enclose space
- minimal cutting waste
- ease of construction with minimal labor and time
- effective thermal color use
- minimal furnishing requirements
- optimized outdoor-space use
- variety of single and multiple units, readily modifiable to fit any climate
- opportunities for self-sufficiency
- visual expansion of interior space
- designs that work for

- condominiums, townhomes, and clusters
- designs that increase marketability
- manufactured and stick-built capability
- minimal exterior and interior maintenance
- considerations for privacy and noise avoidance
- minimal detailing and specialized construction requirements

Categories of Affordable Homes

Five categories of affordable home designs are presented in this book:

(1) compact houses from 500 to 1,000 square feet (46.5 to 92.9 square meters) net livable area;

(2) midsized houses 1,000 to 1,500 square feet (92.9 to 139.4 square meters);

(3) multiples; such as duplexes and townhomes, clustered side-by-sides, and stacked or variable-level homes;

(4) ultracompact houses below 500 square feet (46.5 square meters); and,

(5) survival houses designed for protection against man-made or natural hazards.

Compact. The affordable, compact house plans are designed to be highly agreeable spaces that serve human use. Practical, small-scale furniture and furnishings sustain the concept of "concentrated livability." Although noise and privacy are difficult to control in a small space, these plans give an open, spacious feeling. Some plans have lofts or storage spaces that can be modified for sleeping, studio, home office, or other uses. Furniture must be small in scale, movable, usable, and/or stackable. It needs to look and feel "right" for the space. These compact houses are ideal for singles, young couples, senior citizens, artists, writers, or musicians. They can serve as a guest house, vacation house, or as a separate studio located behind a main house. Though very small, they can accommodate children for limited periods.

Midsized. The midsized plans offer greater space within a minimal footprint. Private space can be used for an office, den, or playroom, or for TV viewing, recreation, arts, crafts, or other hobbies. These midsized plans have two or more bedrooms and practical storage for families, mingles, or people with space-requiring interests.

Multiple. Most of the plans in the foregoing categories can be integrated as duplexes, clusters, townhomes, or other forms of multiple housing. Joining units side by side or vertically decreases heating and cooling needs and increases thermal efficiency. Multiple units climatically buffer each other. In most cases, land costs, maintenance costs, common centralized storage, outdoor facilities, and laundry functions can be shared. As the number of units increases, more extensive recreational areas can be economically provided; e.g., a swimming pool, playground, clubhouse, or assembly room. The density of multiple units impacts human activity day and night, and careful design planning is needed to minimize probabilities of disturbance.

Duplexes can fit people's life-span patterns. A single person or a couple can live in one unit and rent the other to help pay the mortgage. The rental unit provides income tax depreciation and equity from property value escalation, assuming one party holds the duplex mortgage. If children arrive on the scene, they can expand into the adjoining unit. As the children eventually leave home, the person or couple can retire back to the original space and again receive rental income from the other unit. A duplex provides more security than a single-family home to an older couple. When one of the units is occupied, it increases protection from intrusion and loss of possessions for the adjoining unit.

Any social or age group can occupy multiple units. A multiple housing complex lends itself to any societal, cultural, or religious focus or mix.

Ultracompact. All of these designs are under 500 square feet (46.5 square meters) in net livable area. In some cases the houses are so small that they would not meet the space-provision requirements of some building codes; however, these codes may change as space-conserving houses become more common. The chief advantage of the ultracompact houses lies in the minimal amount of materials and labor needed for their construction. These designs could be ideal for vacation or retreat houses, studios, or as add-ons to existing homes.

Survival. The survival house is an answer to the probabilities of hazard. Each design, depending on the protection desired and perceived hazards, strives for day-to-day livability and substantial protection. Natural hazards, such as hurricanes, high winds, tornadoes, and floods can occur in any region. Erratic weather patterns are predicted to continue and possibly at times to reach cataclysmic intensity. These survival houses can also afford some protection in the case of a nuclear incident, provided the home is located near the periphery of the blast zone (30 or more miles [48 kilometers] away). Affordable homes that resist a direct nuclear blast are not feasible. The shelter designs in this book provide a degree of fallout protection, absentee security, and space for food and other supportive needs.

A protective retreat space can be incorporated in the compact, midsized, and ultracompact categories. Emergency provisions and extra structural protection can be designed into the living spaces or basements. Retreat spaces can serve as overflow space or as a food storage shelter.

Principal Uses of Compact Home Designs

Some principal uses of compact home designs are as follows:

- single-family
- duplex
- cluster (condominium or townhome)
- tandem (one residence occupied by two owners, somtimes known as "mingles")
- retirement
- congregate (collective housing for a specific group)
- studio (arts, crafts, music, or other)
- guest quarters
- vacation
- survival
- retreat
- barrier-free
- rental units

- motel units
- lodge units
- medical units
- convalescent units
- military units
- hospice units
- temporary abode
- mobile home alternative
- in-fill housing (on existing sites)
- mixed-use housing (with commercial)
- add-on to existing home
- small office units

New Living Units in Existing Neighborhoods (In-Fill Housing)

In regard to in-fill housing: In many cities, the zoning regulations permit more than one housing unit on one site. This frequently applies to older neighborhoods where freestanding, single-family residences prevail. Usually, such multiple zoning is for attached forms of housing such as duplexes. Generally, accommodation was not made for the addition of another living unit to be built at a later date, although conversions often occur (legally and illegally) for the use of more than one family.

On sites that have the potential for living-unit additions, several of the compact homes of this book could, in most cases, be constructed. Such additions to an existing home should not neglect various considerations; namely, observance of zoning setbacks; impact on existing utilities; easy access for entrance; additional parking requirements; optimizing the passive solar capability of the new unit; effect of the added unit on neighbors; how the design of the existing

home and the new addition might be best joined and made harmonious in function and appearance; and, the economic implications of the new living unit.

If new, unattached living units are allowed, this possibility should be evaluated in terms of improved solar exposure versus the reduction of energy loss by attachment.

Cataclysmic Protection

Scientists and soothsayers have reached a common opinion that our earth is now and will continue to undergo violent and erratic disruptions. Storms of great violence, tornadoes, volcanic eruptions, floods, and angry seas are ushering in a period of erratic and life-threatening conditions.

Compact-size homes offer greater resistance strength to atmospheric violence than those of conventional construction. With concrete basements topped with reinforced concrete, they would offer an effective storm cellar and provide a well-protected place for food storage and water supplies. Such basement space would not only be a refuge from storms but would also have a protective value against nuclear fallout, which could occur not only from a nuclear accident but also from intentional urban sabotage or attack. Reinforced concrete exterior walls can be extended up to the roof line for added protection.

Such homes (with protective earth berms) can be rapidly constructed with relatively unskilled labor and minimal materials as a premeditated protective retreat or as a replacement housing unit after a disaster has struck. The lumber and rubble from a disaster can be a handy resource for construction of these compact homes.

Chapter 2

Site and Microclimate

Buying a site for home construction is a major financial commitment. Not only is the price of the site important, but purchasing a site is a step toward the larger commitment of building a home upon it. The location of the site confers a certain present and future value upon the marketability of the home. Quality of neighborhood, access to schools, churches, stores, medical and other services, recreational and cultural facilities, and to major roadways and airports — as well as on-site solar and utility access — affect the intrinsic value of the home and its site.

A home is a long-term investment. The site should be considered an integral part of the architecture. The more the site can be used to decrease the need for building indoor space, and the more it can be made productive for growing food, the higher is the return on investment. A well-maintained home and site protects the initial investment.

Under zoning regulations, most sites are unnecessarily large. Furthermore, most land planners and developers do not adequately consider solar land planning and solar orientation. Greater-density solar planning with smaller sites requires special attention to location, orientation, and other architectural

needs. More sites per acre decreases the shared cost of utilities, roads, curbs, and storm drainage. However, the smaller the site, the more difficult it is to optimize solar exposure for passive use.

Zero-property-line zoning (in which two separately owned housing units can abut along a common property line) is conducive to high-density residential planning. However, in regard to passive solar, it can be a serious constraint unless solar radiation can be reasonably captured.

In a cold climate where any housing unit is located north of a south-oriented housing unit, the north unit has a passive solar disadvantage. Options for hybrid and/or active solar systems can be limited to the roof or portions of the north unit not in the path of the south unit's shadow.

Smaller sites usually accompany smaller homes in new developments for economic reasons. Smaller sites increase the probabilities of physical disturbance, noise, lack of privacy, likelihood of undesirable odors, and exclusion of some daylight and desired solar radiation. The common practice of using wood-burning equipment to supplement passive and active solar heating is both troublesome and injurious to the neighborhood. The greater the density of a de-

velopment, the more polluted the air is likely to be from wood- or coal-buring equipment.

Site-development density problems can be alleviated by planning and design. The more compact the residential community, the more care is needed to plan and design for human composure, privacy, peace, and stress release. As the density of a neighborhood increases, the use of roof surfaces and outdoor ground-level spaces becomes more important. Thus, the plans of this book illustrate various concepts of site and roof use that should be located and designed to avoid friction with neighbors.

Garages and carports have not been shown with many of the plans. Economics tends to dictate home construction without garages or carports. Where possible, however, the smaller the home, the greater the need for storage space that garages can provide and provision should be made for their construction at a future date (without creating access, site, or architectural problems).

Architectural walls that define outdoor space are more expensive than fencing. Walls act as a visual transition and extension of the architecture into the landscape. They can help to secure and establish territorial boundaries. Site modification with topographic earth berms, vegetation, walls, or fencing can reduce climatic impacts upon the architecture.

Each home site that a person might consider for purchase has to stand on its own merit. A guideline for buying a site, listing many positive and negative factors, can be found at the end of this chapter. In purchasing a site with available sewer and water service, be sure to check into tap and sewer connection fees and how these services will be billed. Whether telephone and electric service is overheard or underground (or is required to be underground) is an economic matter. Poles that carry overhead service are an eyesore, but underground service can be expensive.

Climatic Zones and Microclimate

Most of the designs in this book were conceived for the cold and temperate zones of the United States. The exterior-surface area (roofs and exterior walls) has been minimized (but livability maximized) to reduce climatic exposure and insulation cost. The regional aspect of climatic zones is the key to the design, but microclimatic conditions of the site should not be neglected.

The principal forces of climate are sun and wind that affect temperature and humidity of the site and the architecture. The more that architecture and site may be formed to use these natural forces and control their climatic and microclimatic influences, the more clearly defined will be the architectural aesthetic. Architectural design regionalism is not new but rather is evident in human cultures throughout the world, shaped to particular climatic-response and survival strategies.

Each climatic zone of the continental United States, together with all world climatic zones, offer environmental benefits as well as problems.

The five major regional climatic zones in the continental United States are:

Cold Zone. Northern areas of the United States and mountain regions extending toward the south.

Temperate Zone. A major thermal zone extending laterally across the United States.

Hot-Arid Zone. Southern desert areas, dry and hot.

Hot-Humid Zone. Southern coastal areas along the Atlantic Ocean and Gulf of Mexico.

Cool-Humid Zone. Northern coastal areas along the Pacific Ocean.

Every site is influenced by the regional climate. The five zones shown above are further subdivided in the appendix into sixteen, more specific climate types. A map displays the location of these zones and is accompanied by their basic heating and cooling guidelines.

The *specific microclimate* of the site is of greatest importance. Precipitation, terrain, vegetation, degree of solar exposure, wind patterns, the presence of water bodies, geology, and the influences of buidings or other built forms on or near the site create unique, site-specific, climatic conditions. "Regional climatic factors are always tempered at the local level by the physical composition of elements on the site."[2] There is no substitute for accurate and complete microclimatic data on the site itself for effective, integrated design.

[2] American Institute of Architects, *Energy in Design: Techniques* (Washington, D.C.: AIA, 1981), p. 4.1.

In making a comprehensive profile of the site's microclimate, analysis of climatic data from the site, the area, and the region is needed. Regional data (in addition to that mentioned above) is listed in the reference section of this book. Area data is also available from universities, state energy commissions, the Tennessee Valley Authority (for areas within its jurisdiction), and the Air Force. Local weather data is available from the National Oceanic and Atmospheric Administration. NOAA is the national weather service, with hundreds of weather stations across the country. Each local weather station can provide information in various formats and time periods.

A fact to remember is that climatic conditions at a specific site can vary considerably from the local weather data. Site features can cause modifications in temperatures, wind velocity and direction, precipitation, humidity, and the amount of solar radiation. Knowledge of the specific microclimatic conditions can come from observation of the site itself · and the neighboring influences, and discussions with knowledgeable people about particular climatic factors. Application of natural physical laws concerning energy transfers, solar radiation, air movement, and the thermal characteristics of the earth and atmosphere are essential to concept resolutions and appropriate design.

Site Analysis Factors

There are four basic areas to consider when analyzing a site's microclimate:

1. Site Location and Solar Orientation. South slopes are the preferred location for maximum solar gain in winter heating. A south slope will receive more radiation than

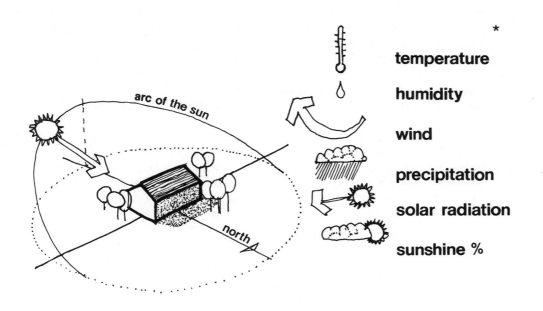

temperature

humidity

wind

precipitation

solar radiation

sunshine %

a flat site. North-facing slopes are best when cooling is the major consideration. An east slope is preferred over west, since it will receive the maximum amount of morning solar radiation. West slopes receive maximum afternoon sun and intensive solar impacts in the summer. In the context of solar radiation, the site should be analyzed to determine if any direct sun or stabilized, thermal air pockets exist. These are caused by topography, on-site or neighboring buildings, or other forms than can occur in a contained, urban or rural setting or within a forest enclave. The shading effects of site elements (topography, vegetation, built forms) need to be reviewed for any possible obstruction of solar radiation. Shading on the east and west, however, can create a summer advantage for outdoor use and activity. The reflectivity of surrounding buildings can produce undesirable glare and heat and can increase the need for cooling. Intense solar reflection, such as low-angled sun on a water body, can greatly increase visual glare. Air pollution, mists, and fog will affect the amount and composition of sunlight reaching a site.

2. Wind Patterns and Movement and Ground-Current Convection. On-site topography, vegetation, structures, and fencing can greatly affect wind direction, intensity, and air pressure. Wind produces a windchill factor in winter. It increases cooling and comfort in the summer. Energy-conscious site design employs topography, vegetation, existing buildings, and forms to block or channel breezes to increase conservation and human comfort.

On sloping terrain and in hilly or mountainous areas, masses of cold air created by radiative cooling of the ground slide downward and settle in valleys and lowlands, creating cold-air pockets. Slopes warmed by the sun during the day release heat to the atmosphere, causing convective upward air movement. At night, the air flow reverses. Cliffs and steep areas of bare rock warmed by the sun can produce substantial thermal updrafts.

Flat, open plains and large water bodies do not impede wind except by friction and turbulence. Sloping ground diverts wind flow. Forested areas are calm. Arid regions are typically windy and more turbulent, because of the dry-ground responses to solar radiation, convection, and conduction. However, if the ground is moist or vegetation well watered, the atmosphere will be quieter, because the bulk of the radiation is used in evapotranspiration.

3. Water and Water Bodies. Water bodies exert a moderating influence on climate conditions. Because of its high long-term heat capacity, water will even out temperature swings and serve to temper surrounding areas. However, the additional humidity in the air can be a detriment to summer comfort and increase the chilling effect of damp winds in winter. In general, water is warmer relative to atmospheric temperatures in winter and at night and relatively cooler in the summer and during the day. Site drainage can have an impact on economics and optimized energy design. Available well, river, or lake water can be used as a heat sink and heat source for heat-exchanger and heat-pump systems. On-site water pooling can also be developed into solar ponds. Retention systems, such as ponds or cisterns, should be used to save valuable water from rain and snow accumulation. This reduces runoff and can supply irrigation water for food production and other on-site vegetation. In arid regions, water in the path of incoming winds will provide evaporative cooling. In humid regions, standing puddles should be avoided and any water collection should drain away from a house, out of the path of wind.

4. Earth and Land Forms. The nature of the earth surface and the soil at a specific site can affect energy exchanges on the ground surface and between the conductive and albedo (reflection) characteristics. These in turn affect ground temperatures, which affect the surface air temperatures. The earth's surface configuration and natural features affect the amount and intensity of solar radiation received at a specific site. Hills, cliffs, and mountains can block sunlight on northern slopes, and the landform itself can produce shadows. Shaded slopes can be as much as 5 to 15 degrees Fahrenheit (2.8 to 8.3 degrees Celsius) cooler than exposed slopes. Vegetation acts as an insulative cover, providing shade to the ground and also moderating incoming ra-

diation by reflection, scattering, and absorption. Vegetation serves as an evaporative field, releasing moisture to the air. Plants act as air-filtration systems, cleaning and purifying the air by absorbing carbon dioxide and returning oxygen. Plants also trap and remove dust and particulate matter and airborne gases. Carbon monoxide, a serious pollutant (primarily from automobile exhaust), is converted to carbon dioxide (useful to plants) by soil microorganisms. Abundant vegetation improves all moderate-to-dry microclimates, but can have an adverse comfort effect upon very humid site locations.

Earth can be an effective moderator of the climate. Its thermal mass, topographic form, and barrier effect should be exploited to enhance temperature stability, control wind and air movement, and act as a climatic buffer. These thermal benefits apply to each thermal zone when the architecture is designed and appropriately located, oriented, and formed as an element of the earth itself.

The basic design problem of the site is

how to situate the architecture to optimize solar and other natural energies; how, if possible, to preserve the site's ecologic balance; and, how to modify the site and form the architecture to attenuate climatic extremes. Beyond these fundamentals, site development and construction should enhance the attributes of neighboring sites and, in dry and moderately dry areas, retain on-site surface water for practical use. Environmental quietness and privacy, vehicular access, visual screening, and solar warmth or shading for driveways and parking areas should not be neglected and should respectively relate to cold or warm climates and seasonal change. In energy terms, every site is unique and every architectural project is unique to its site. To optimize functional space use, human vitality, investment value, and minimal nonrenewable energy demand requires astute thermal-zone design.

Landscaping

Landscaping is a very important factor in energy-conscious site development. Astute planting of trees and vegetation can influence on-site wind patterns, increasing comfort in summer and winter by channeling or blocking seasonal breezes. Landscaping affects the scale and texture of a site and home. It can serve as a foreground or background element, influencing the total visual composition of the site. Landscaping can also be a visual screen, blocking off objectionable views and increasing privacy.

Native vegetation and use of ground covers, instead of grass, can save water, money, fertilizer, maintenance, and energy. "Edible" landscaping that produces fruits, nuts, or

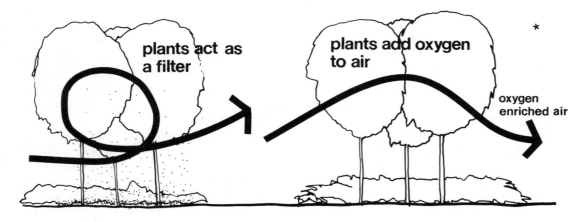

plants act as a filter

plants add oxygen to air

*

oxygen enriched air

berries can supplement a home food supply. Select landscaping to harmonize with the climate of the area and to fit with the specific site characteristics, such as soil type, water availability, natural contours, and seasonal growth patterns. Try to retain prevailing ecologic site conditions where possible that remain in phase with climate-control objectives.

Topographic Survey, Soils Tests, Percolation Tests

A site survey is usually required by the building department of a municipality. Give attention to the available utilities (sewer, water, electricity) and to drainage or local storm-runoff requirements. Most codes do not permit surface water to drain onto neighboring properties.

For other than nearly flat sites, a topographic survey is needed if the on-site grades vary to a significant degree. Large trees or any significant vegetation scheduled to remain for the completed project should be plotted on the topographic survey. Any fencing or neighboring buildings that might intrude on the site should be noted. Also plot unobstructed solar access and seasonal sun angles. The influence of contours and vegetation on wind movement and seasonal wind patterns should be a part of the site analysis. Any future changes in site or neighboring conditions that could alter solar access or natural air movement over the site need to be considered.

Soils tests may be required for building-construction-plan approval. These tests also provide information needed for the design of architectural footings and foundations. When soils tests are performed, water tables should be checked relative to seasonal conditions. Any subsurface geological formations that might affect drainage or excavation, such as weathered or dense-rock strata, should also be checked. Subsurface conditions are especially important for earth-sheltered or underground construction. Soil testing should be performed by experienced firms with recognized ability. Any tests should be made at the actual building location, not just anywhere on the site. A way to save money is to employ a licensed engineer to perform the soils test and also design the footings and foundation (or other construction to meet structural requirements).

If a septic system and drainage field are needed, percolation tests must be performed to determine the soil suitability and the location of the drainage field to meet health codes and regulations. Sanitary sewer invert depths should be considered. The calculated fall from underground or basement toilets to the sewer should not be less than $\frac{1}{8}$ inch to the foot, preferably $\frac{1}{4}$ to the foot (or as required to meet minimum code conditions).

Where bentonite clay exists (which is expandable with moisture), there can be a problem with uplifting soil. Grade beams (lateral, subsurface, concrete beams usually supported on caissons) can require a compressible void to avert uplift fractures. Basement floors that rest on bentonite (or over other expandable soils) should be independent of the structure. Interior partitions that might be subject to uplifting pressures should be treated as slip joints at the ceiling line to avoid internal, structural damage. Unstable soils conditions require engineering solutions by a competent, licensed engineer.

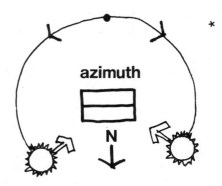

A solar site survey tool can be used or scale drawings be plotted to determine existing obstructions to direct solar access. Furthermore, information relative to zoning restrictions or other factors should be gathered regarding the possibilities of future partial or complete loss of solar access. The ultimate development of the site or sites must be initially considered so that solar access — particularly for passive solar use — remains protected and unobstructed.

For a passive solar system to function properly, complete, unimpeded solar radiation to the system should exist through all periods of the heating season. Check the solar elevation (altitude) at its lowest point on the winter solstice (on or about December 21) from nine o'clock in the morning to three o'clock in the afternoon. Solar radiation should be unobstructed on this date and also not blocked by neighboring obstructions throughout the heating season.

Solar Site Planning for Single-Family and Multifamily Housing

Solar planning for a new, single-family home or home addition requires particular

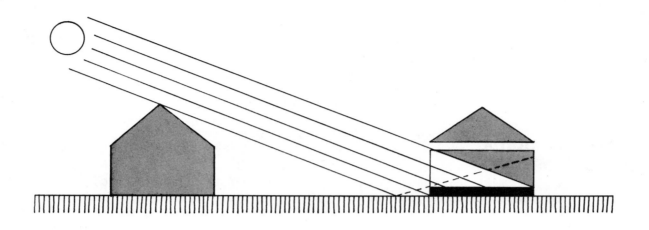

Fig. 1. Separation Distance

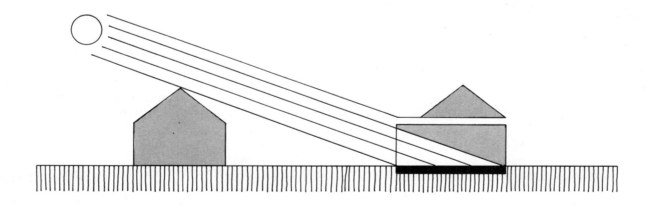

Fig. 2. Separation Distance With Sunspace

attention to unobstructed, wintertime solar access. Unless an entire community is composed of underground homes, an acceptable winter solar access might prove difficult to attain. Existing buildings, trees, or other solar access obstructions south of a projected passive solar home can negate the use of south-wall exposure or reduce its effective performance.

The drawings that accompany this discussion clearly demonstrate the effect of winter sun (illustrated at a 20-degree angle, which should be adjusted to your latitude). Note the considerable separation distance required for direct solar radiation to clear the roof ridge of a one-story, conventional house and penetrate into a sunspace or main level of a new passive solar residence in figures 1, 2, and 3. Earth-sheltering, when the main residence level is below the prevailing grade, increases the separation distance even more (figs. 4 and 5).

South glazing on the second floor of a two-story house with an intervening, horizontal, floor/ceiling mass that can radiate heat gains above and below allows for closer proximity to a south one-story structure, tree, or other equally tall obstruction (fig. 6). Maximum closeness between housing units can be achieved by using the roof areas for passive, active, and hybrid solar collection (fig. 7). Active solar systems should not be neglected as an economically viable possibility. They have the advantage of an effective time-period delay in the use of stored solar-thermal energy.

The ground surface can reflect 50 percent of the incident solar radiation and it can be made more reflective with white-painted patio pavers or brick or white marble chips as conditions may allow. Such reflective advantages can be improved by greater distance between the house that shades and the one being shaded. Keep in mind that the greater the amount of solar energy than can be collected and/or stored by optimizing the area of solar collection, the greater the opportunity to maximize solar use.

The smaller sites and minimized street frontage of housing developments make it

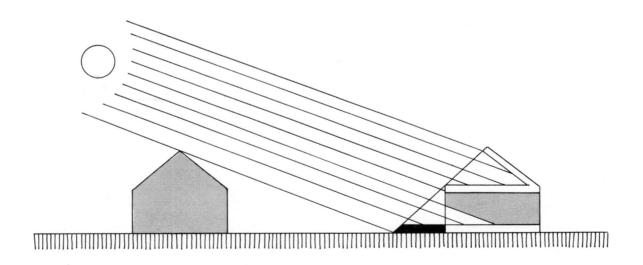

Fig. 3. Separation Distance With Sunspace and Sloping Glass

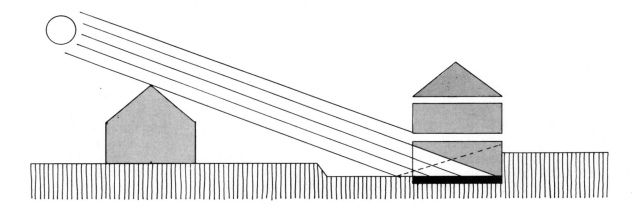

Fig. 4. Separation Distance With Earth-Shelter Only

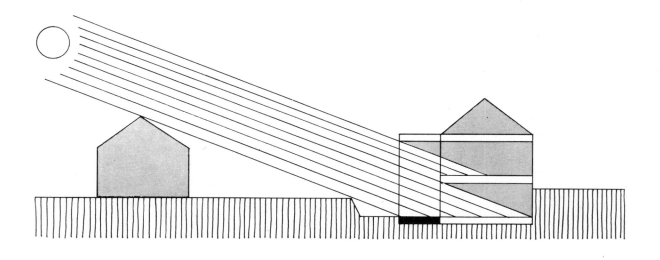

Fig. 5. Separation Distance With Earth-Shelter With Sunspace

more difficult to plan for the most effective passive solar use. The schematic, block-planning layouts reveal primary problems when using exterior, south-wall solar concepts.

In figure 8, sites on conventional east-west streets have good wintertime passive solar exposure. Solar access benefits by the width of the street, front setbacks, and a double backyard depth. In figure 9, zero-property-line zoning on east-west streets provides added side-yard space well suited for outdoor, patio living. The south-wall, passive solar opportunities remain unchanged. Attached garages or carports can also be located in the side-yard space without blocking southside solar radiation.

In figure 10, still with east-west streets, the sites are increased in number. Thus, they are smaller, and the living units are attached townhomes. The singular advantage is less total energy loss than that of single-family homes. Solar collection opportunities remain effective unless garages are attached to the south frontage on the south side of the block. Garages can be attached to the northern row of townhomes with direct access to the street without disrupting solar access.

In figure 11, with a north-south street axis, only the living units at the south end of the block are apt to receive full wintertime solar access. With narrow sites, all other units would have to use a roof type of passive or active solar collection. Roof heights and angles have to be carefully planned to avoid solar obstruction. Garages can be attached with street access. Rear patios can have good, south, solar exposure.

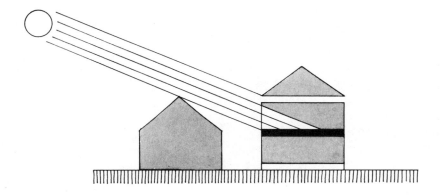

Fig. 6. Separation Distance Decreased

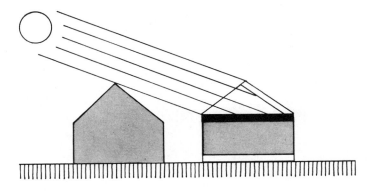

Fig. 7. Solar Attic or Roof System

In figure 12, the offset, zero-property-line, single-family arrangement avoids some of the visual monotony but not the morning and afternoon solar interference of each half of the units on the north-south street axis. Garages attached to the north, east, or west sides of the units will tend to create a planning problem.

In figure 13, a very high-density siting plan with north-south streets and staggered living units increases passive solar opportunities. Unless an alley is provided, at-

tached garages will be a problem for half of the living units.

In figure 14, the north-south-axis street plan creates solar exposure problems for the single-family homes. Attached-garage street access would be easily accomplished. By changing the direction of the street to east-west and rotating the single-family units to north and south, south-wall, passive solar opportunities would be much improved and attached garages could still be used.

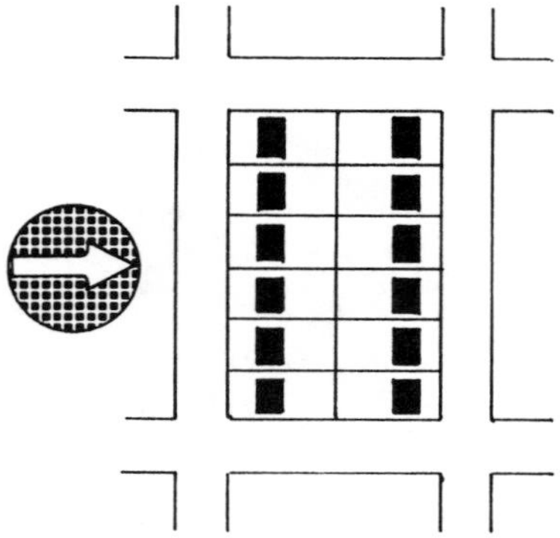

Fig. 8

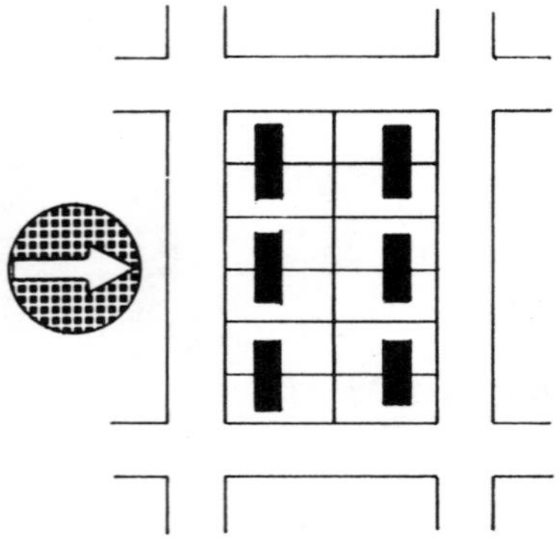

Fig. 9

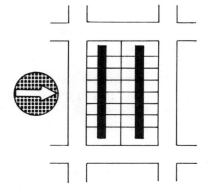

Fig. 10

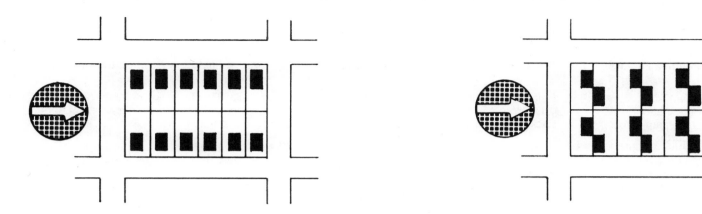

Fig. 11

Fig. 12

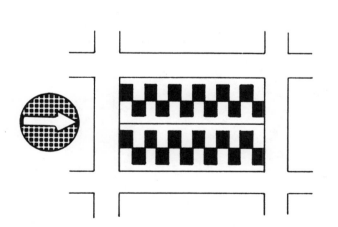

Fig. 13

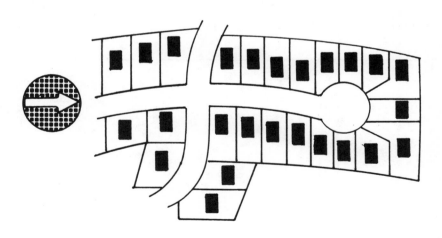

Fig. 14

25

Checklist Guideline to Buying a Site

Negative Factors	Positive Factors	Negative Factors	Positive Factors	Negative Factors	Positive Factors
Air Pollution	Clean Air	Neighborhood in Decline	Neighborhood on the Rise	Unavailability of Economic Labor	Availability of Economic Labor
Water Pollution	Pure Water	Lack of Privacy	Privacy from Neighbors	Site Remote from Stores	Site Convenient to Stores
Earth Contamination	Uncontaminated Earth	Obstruction of Direct Sunlight	Unobstructed Sunlight	Site Remote from Services	Site Convenient to Services
Poor Soils Conditions	Good Soils Conditions	Difficult Site Topography	Favorable Site Topography	Lack of Good Schools	Good Schools
Lack of Existing Vegetation	Useful Existing Grasses, Trees, Shrubs	Poor Access to Site	Good Access to Site		
		Difficult Access for Construction	Easy Construction Access	Easements on Property	No Easements
Density of Site Vegetation	Minimal Site Preparatory Cost	Lack of Adequate Utilities	Adequate Utilities	Restrictive Covenants	Nonrestrictive Covenants
Rock Outcroppings	Absence of Surface Problems	High Utility Rates	Favorable Utility Rates	Contrary Zoning Restrictions	Favorable Zoning Restrictions
Subsurface Rock	Absence of Subsurface Problems	Expensive Water and Sewer Tap Fees	Low-Cost Water and Sewer Tap Fees	Far from Employment	Close to Employment
		Site Too Small for Project	Site Adequately Large	Unfavorable Tax Structure	Favorable Taxation
Subsurface Water	Useful Water, and Not a Problem	Site Too Restrictive	Adaptable Site	Comparable Cost of Site	Cost at or Below Market Value
Poor Drainage	Good Drainage	Material Supply Far Away	Convenient Materials Supply	Site-to-Building Cost Ratio	Acceptable Economic Cost Ratio
Lack of Quietness	Quiet Neighborhood				

Chapter 3

Design and Architecture

Total, Integrative Design

The conceptual plans and designs presented in this book embody total, integrative energy design. Integrative design is not a new concept. It appears in traditional as well as avant-garde design movements. Some current architects and designers individually or as a group have engaged in integrative design of land planning, architecture, and architectural interiors (including furniture and furnishings). Within architecture, configurations, forms, colors, and textures are repeated as thematic design elements. Contemporary and classic designs of furniture, lighting fixtures, fabrics, and floor coverings have originated with architects and designers as integrative elements of a total architecture.

Add to this design approach the concept that everything is a form of energy and exhibits its own unique thermal, atmospheric, light-responsive, gravitational, ionic, magnetic, physical, and symbolic properties. In this regard, integrative *energy* design can have far-reaching functional and economic importance. As we shape and form materials by design and develop their use as or into systems, we endow them with an initial and ongoing energy commitment.

In the case of architecture with its long period of protective existence for human activities and use, each option and commitment to design that we make prescribes to a large extent an inbuilt energy-demand factor. Thus, if a residential design can save any portion of energy initially used in its materials and construction and further minimize operational and maintenance energy, our conceptual and implementation efforts are not in vain.

Not to be overlooked is the influence of design on human behavior. As we design a home or a product we condition people into a responsive behavior pattern. Placement of partitions, doorways, stairways, furniture, lighting, or even light switches controls the behavior of people and translates into an amount of energy usage.

Total, integrative, energy design controls life-cycle energy costs, biophysical-space adaptiveness, and states of human health and vitality. Total, integrative, energy design allows a prospective home owner and his/her architect to weigh all of the costs and benefits and exercise appropriate options — be they matters of landscaping, architecture, the interior, or the effect upon the home owner and other occupants of the dwelling.

Compact Home Scale

There is little question that compact homes have a small-scale exterior appearance compared to conventional dwellings; however, astute use of exterior landscaping, garden walls, fencing, patios, arbors, garages, and carports — together with the joining of units into duplexes, clusters, or townhomes — can produce both an agreeable scale and an intimate relationship to the earth. Expanding the roof lines and volume can create a larger sense of scale and a homey look. In design terms, it is equivalent to putting a large hat (roof) on the home. It also will substantially increase costs for material and labor.

The scaling of lots compatible to the compact home and discretionary, solar-oriented placement of housing units will have a critical effect upon the total textural matrix of a development. Greater density of compact units creates a smaller scale and overall community texture than that generated by larger housing units with larger sites. Site planning subtleties become more important as living units decrease in size.

One design problem is the proportional scale of the automobile. Compact cars certainly are more appropriate with compact homes, as are midsized cars with midsized homes. Carports and garages scaled to the smaller car represent a better architectural balance to the proportions of the smaller home. Large-size cars will result in a visual and physical accommodation problem. Numerous homes in this book do not materially cover a ground space greater than that required for a garage for two large-size cars.

Street and site orientations to the sun and overall density planning should not neglect adequate solar access for all housing units. Landscaping and fencing can obstruct passive solar gains. Various forms of common land-area space should augment solar as well as controlled wind-pattern siting, landscaping, and architectural design resolutions. See "Solar Site Planning" in Chapter 2.

Plan Configurations

Square Plans. The further a site location is north in the northern hemisphere or south in the southern hemisphere, the more a square plan, with its minimal exterior surface to interior volume of space, is advantageous. Domes have the least exterior surface to the atmosphere relative to their interior volume. However, because of the loss of peripheral headroom in small domes and problems of rectangular furniture not fitting well within a curve, a small square or rectangle (with vertical exterior walls) provides the most economical and useful interior space. Olgyay, in his book *Design with Climate,* clearly shows the climatic benefits of narrower east-west elevations; longer north-south elevations are more effective as the site lies closer to the equator. Nevertheless, in the interest of minimal cost

and other factors, a square plan is preferred.

The other factors are that minimal materials and labor for enclosure, partitions, circulatory waste space, foundation area, roof area, electrical and mechanical distribution distances, floor covering, paint, and furnishings are required. There is less interior volume to heat, cool, and ventilate. Since many of the designs presented in this book are about the size of a normal double-car garage, this provides a structural and common-enclosure wall of adequate dimension for an attached carport or garage.

A square, compact, passive solar home can be oriented to the south regardless of north-south or east-west street direction and property access. For some of the square plans, the roof can be turned 90 degrees to accommodate active or passive solar needs but with the entry door facing the street or a side entry on either the east or west. In single-site or site-development planning, a square plan with controlled roof lines can minimize obstruction of solar accss to other homes located to the north, east, or west.

Along with the foregoing economic, solar, and practical advantages of square plans, a few negative factors should be considered. Many people do not like boxy architecture; however, attractive roof lines, landscaping, and exterior walls can help relieve this aesthetic objection. A square architectural form tends to look smaller than a rectangular plan of equal square footage. Although a diminutive appearance might bother some potential home owners, astute site planning for a single unit, a cluster, or an entire housing development — plus greater density and attached units — can create a very appealing texture of habitation

and landscaping. The minimal interior volume makes indoor air pollution more critical in compact, square homes. Consult the section on indoor air quality for solutions to this problem (Chapter 6).

Rectangular plans more readily adaptable to climatic and solar response depend upon latitude for their optimal proportional configuration. A rectangular-plan home is more energy efficient, but a square plan is usually less costly to build.

Rectangular Plans. A rectangle is a more energy-efficient climatic shape, depending upon the latitude in which a home is located. The length of the south face of a house will increase and the end dimension decrease to reach an optimal energy-efficient proportion as the location advances southward. The ideal proportions are illustrated in Olgyay's *Design with Climate.*

A rectangular home improves the possibilities for effective passive solar collection and solar-thermal storage. A greater roof area than the square plan is also available for the active solar collection. A longer south face for a home that faces the street either to the south or north requires a larger site width than a square plan of comparable floor area. When the site has an east or west frontage, a rectangular plan can use a narrower site than that of an equal-area square plan. A simple rectangular plan with a rectangular roof form that has no offsetting breaks can be economical to construct, particularly if it is carefully dimensioned to match standard material sizes.

Triangular Plans. Triangular plan forms can produce some sharp interior corners difficult to clean and furnish. Foundation and roof intersections can increase the complexity and cost of construction. Nevertheless, internal and external triangular forms do stimulate visual excitement.

Most roofs have a triangular form superimposed upon a rectangular or square architectural plan. The triangle is the most efficient form prevailing against the force of gravity. A roof truss and R. Buckminster Fuller's geodesic dome depend on the structural integrity of the triangle. Roof trusses have been used most often to provide a structural span and a climate-protective roof form. Unfortunately, roof-truss members often interrupt the most effective use of the resultant attic space. Required ventilation of attic spaces also tends to produce exfiltration and energy loss from interior living spaces. High ceilings most often are angular to fit with roof angles that are not only visually beguiling but allow for a larger available interior air volume within the building envelope. High ceilings also provide an opportunity for both useful wintertime destratification and summertime inductive ventilation. It is also possible to interject useful loft and balcony spaces within the angular ceiling lines that are high enough for headroom.

Triangular architectural forms produce a greater amount of cutting waste than square or rectangular plan homes but can, within a compact limit, increase passive solar capability and divert cold, winter winds.

Circular Plans. Primitive and indigenous construction frequently uses a circular form where low-cost manual labor is plentiful. Cylindrical, conical, and barrel-vault structures characterize small dwellings in many parts of the world. In our own intensive-labor-cost society, circular or curved architectural forms exceed the cost of those that are square, rectangular, or triangular. To lay out and create circular foundations, walls, roofs, colonnades, doorways, windows, or other architectural elements generally increases the cost twofold or more than linear forms.

The lowest-cost building structure based on the circle is likely to be a geodisic dome constructed of plywood. The advantage of the dome is its structural efficiency, low exterior-surface-to-volume ratio, and relative low cost when made of manufactured sections. The disadvantages are constraints upon interior partition, cabinet, and furniture placement and often inadequate interior headroom near the periphery of the dome. A small dome, particularly, loses its natural architectural attractiveness when it is insensitively penetrated by doors, windows, or dormers.

Cylindrical masonry walls or vaulted structures are less costly to construct than concrete structures but require engineered placement of reinforcement bars. To form curves in wood construction requires special sawing, bending, or laminating.

More on Plan Configurations

More complex plan configurations (other than square, rectangular, circular, or triangular) will be more costly to build and more involved in the construction of roof, foundation, and framing. L-shaped or U-shaped plans have a less advantageous volume-to-surface ratio from a temperate- or cold-climate standpoint. However, if nonsolar elevations are minimized (east, west, and north), a more complex southside form will increase solar gain because of the increased south-wall surface area.

An important point concerning affordability: The configuration of the perimeter plan enclosure has more to do with the cost of a dwelling than any other single, fundamental architectural element other than the use of complex and expensive materials and interior appointments. Everytime the foundation, outer wall, or roof line is broken, the cost is increased (even if the interior square footage is the same) without necessarily any additional benefit to livability and interior space function.

One way to increase interior space is by cantilevered upper-floor levels that project over the perimeter walls. These do not greatly increase the cost if they are placed in the direction of structural support and foundation and roof lines remain square or rectangular. Such projections usually do not exceed 4 feet (1.2 meters). The resulting overhang can become an effective shading element for the lower level, but take care to avoid undesired shading on passive solar elements.

Codes and Regulations

All provisions of your local zoning regulations and building codes should be adhered to for your residence. The *Uniform Building Code* is used either directly or as a model for most building codes. Inasmuch as the interpretation of building codes may vary with municipalities, it is advised that you ask for rulings to clarify your planning and design.

A few excerpts from the UBC code covering major architectural design factors are presented:

"Every sleeping room below the fourth story shall have at least one operable window or exterior door approved for emergency egress or rescue. The units shall be operable from the inside to provide a full clear opening without the use of separate tools.

"All egress or rescue windows from sleeping rooms shall have a minimum net clear opening of 5.7 square feet. The minimum net clear opening height dimension shall be 24 inches. The minimum net clear opening width dimension shall be 20 inches. Where windows are provided as a means of egress or rescue they shall have a finished sill height not more than 44 inches above the floor."[3]

". . . a dwelling unit shall be provided with natural light by means of exterior glazed openings with an area not less than one-tenth of the floor area of such rooms with a minimum of 10 square feet."[4]

". . . rooms within a dwelling unit shall be provided with natural ventilation by means of openable exterior openings with an area of not less than one-twentieth of the floor area of such rooms with a minimum of 5 square feet.

"In lieu of required exterior openings for natural ventilation, a mechanical ventilating system may be provided. Such a system shall be capable of providing two air changes per hour . . . One-fifth of the air supply shall be taken from the outside."[5]

"For the purpose of determining light and ventilation requirements, any room may be considered as a portion of an adjoining room when one-half of the area of the common wall is open and unobstructed and provides an opening of not less than one-tenth of the floor area of the interior room or 25 square feet, whichever is greater.

Required exterior openings for natural light and ventilation shall open directly onto a street or public alley or a yard or court located on the same lot as the building.

Exception: Required windows may open into a roofed porch where the porch (1) abuts a street, yard, or court; and (2) has a ceiling height of not less than 7 feet; and (3) has the longer side at least 65 percent open and unobstructed."[6]

"Habitable space shall have a ceiling height of not less than 7 feet 6 inches except as otherwise permitted in this section. Kitchens, halls, bathrooms and toilet compartments may have a ceiling height of not less than 7 feet measured to the lowest projection from the ceiling."[7]

"If any room in a building has a sloping ceiling, the prescribed ceiling height for the room is required in only one-half of the area thereof. No portion of the room measuring less than 5 feet from the finished floor to the finished ceiling shall be included in any computation of the minimum area thereof."[8]

"Every dwelling unit shall have at least one room which shall have not less than 150 square feet of floor area. Other habitable rooms except kitchens shall have an area of not less than 70 square feet."[9]

"Every dwelling unit and guest room shall be provided with heating facilities capable of maintaining a room temperature of 70°F at a point 3 feet above the floor in all habitable rooms."[10]

"All bathrooms, water closet compartments, laundry rooms and similar rooms shall be provided with natural ventilation by means of openable exterior openings with an area not less than one-twentieth of the floor area of such rooms with a minimum of 1½ square feet or, in bathrooms, water closet compartments, laundry rooms and similar rooms a mechanical ventilation system connected directly to the outside, capable of providing five air changes per hour, shall be provided."[11]

"An efficiency dwelling unit shall conform to the requirements of the code except as herein provided: (1) The unit shall have a living room of not less than 220 square feet of superficial floor area. An additinal 100 square feet of superficial floor area shall be provided for each occupant of such unit in excess of two. (2) The units shall be provided with a separate closet. (3) The unit shall be provided with a kitchen sink, cooking appliance and refrigeration facilities, each having a clear working space of not less than 30 inches in front. Light and ventilation conforming to this code shall be provided. (4) The unit shall be provided with a separate bathroom containing a water closet, lavatory and bathtub or shower."[12]

"In Group 4, Division 3 Occupancies (dwellings and lodging houses) and in private stairways within individual units of Group R, Division 1 Occupancies (hotels and apartment houses) spiral stairways may be installed. Such stairways may be used for required exits when the area served is limited to 400 square feet.

"The tread must provide a clear walking area measuring at least 26 inches from the outer edge of the supporting column to the inner edge of the handrail. A run of at least 7½ inches is to be provided at a point 12 inches from where the tread is narrowest. The rise must be sufficient to provide 6-foot 6-inch headroom. The rise shall not exceed 9½ inches.

"Handrails shall be placed not less than 30 inches nor more than 34 inches above the nosing of treads"[13]

"Open guardrail and stair railings shall have intermediate rails on an ornamental pattern such that a sphere 9 inches in

[3]*Uniform Building Code: 1979 Edition,* prepared by the International Conference of Building Officials (Whittier, Calif.; International Conference of Building Officials, 1979), section 1204, pp. 85-86.

[4]Ibid., section 1205, p. 86.

[5]Ibid.

[6]Ibid., section 1205, p. 86

[7]Ibid., section 1207, pp. 87-88

[8]Ibid., section 1207, p. 88.

[9]Ibid.

[10]Ibid., section 1211, p. 89

[11]Ibid., section 1205, p. 87

[12]Ibid., section 1208, p. 88

[13]Ibid., section 3305, pp. 505, 506.

diameter cannot pass through. Exceptions: Guardrails for Group R, Division 3 Occupancies may be 36 inches in height; interior guardrails within individual dwelling units or guest rooms of Group R, Division 1 Occupancies may be 36 inches in height."[14]

Residential guardrails should not be less than 36 inches high with spacing of spandrels not more than 9 inches apart. In addition to these factors, all windows that have less than an 18-inch bulkhead are required to have tempered glass; glass that extends to the floor has this requirement also.

All provisions that deal with stoves or fireplaces should be specifically determined by the manufacturer and approved by the building department.

Design Assumptions and Considerations

Certain assumptions and considerations have been made in the design of these homes for most of the plans and designs:

- for the location, orientation, configuration, placement and size of windows or skylights, unobstructed solar radiation prevails for wintertime passive solar heaing;
- the path of solar energy remains unobstructed in the future;
- the actual realities of the site are accommodated by the architect or designer to fit with the topography, road access, vegetation, other structures, and neighboring conditions;
- architectural drawings for construc-

[14]Ibid., section 1716, p. 99

tion based upon the concept plans and designs presented must meet all zoning and code regulations that specifically apply to the jurisdictional location;
- architectural construction drawings using the concepts presented will incorporate the most economic, practical, and energy-conserving local materials, methods, and architectural and engineering resolutions;
- the architect or designer will have the competence to optimize the passive and active solar and other natural, passive energy systems and conservation design consistent with the specifics of the owner's need, scale of the project, the microclimate, year-round solar insolation, and earth-use factors;
- as housing units might be combined into duplexes, cluster homes, or townhomes, all of the foregoing design concerns as well as the larger, practical, energy and economic implications of combining the units should be considered;
- all of the conceptual drawings presented are based on the materials and minimum construction waste economy of a 4-foot (1.2 meter) module although, in some cases, for practical purposes, a 2-foot (.61 meter) increment has been used; thus, a greenhouse might be 6 feet (1.8 meters) deep, or an overall building dimension might be 22 feet (6.7 meters). In any case, standarized doors, windows, and other items should be carefully dimensioned into the final construction drawing;
- for economy, off-the-shelf and stan-

darized items have been considered in the plans and designs;
- exceptions to standardization are because of the great importance of optimizing the interior usefulness and capability of space, such as kitchen cabinets 30 inches (76 centimeters) deep.

The more a design can optimize livability, practicality, ecologic viability, minimal injury to the environment, self-sufficiency, and minimal maintenance, the more effective it will be. Design options should be holistically considered in regard to conceptual organization and life-cycle costs present in landscaping, architecture, and interior furnishings. Energy-sensitive planning for interior, functional space needs and external site use is fundamental to design.

Design and Architectural Features, Guidelines, and Energy Factors

Orientation. Within the boundaries of a site and legal setback restrictions, a house should be located to optimize passive solar energy use. In any case, for small sites, placing a passive solar home as close to the north as possible may be necessary. This could obstruct solar exposure to a passive home that might be on the next adjacent site to the north. Where a south-facing wall cannot be used, a south-facing roof can be designed to perform a passive, hybrid, or active solar function. For conventionally sized sites, the small land coverage of the homes presented increases the possibilities of effective passive solar use. In all cases, a house's passive solar system should face due south or not be rotated more than 20 degrees from the south-face axis.

Views to the west or north can be troublesome. Intense west summer sun can be a problem, as can north views that expose windows to cold winter winds. Minimizing or eliminating fenestration on these elevations and other architectural solutions can alleviate these problems. Placing a home broadside to the west with large glass windows is not the answer to visual or thermal comfort.

Configurations and Interior Planning. All of the homes presented in this book have a tight planning configuration. Design care has been exercised to favor perfectly square or straight-line foundations. Every break or offset in a foundation interrupts the regularity of the forming system and such placement of reinforcement further increases foundation costs. All plan layouts recognize the climate's effect as to daylighting and thermal-solar gains. For parts of the United States that have cool or cold winters, living and dining areas are placed to the south, as they are most adaptable to passive solar gains. Bedrooms, bathrooms, and kitchens are mostly located to the north. Bedrooms can be cooler. Kitchens tend to develop their own heat from cooking and refrigeration. Lofts and upper-level room spaces will tend to overheat because heat rises. Destratification systems are recommended to equalize internal temperatures.

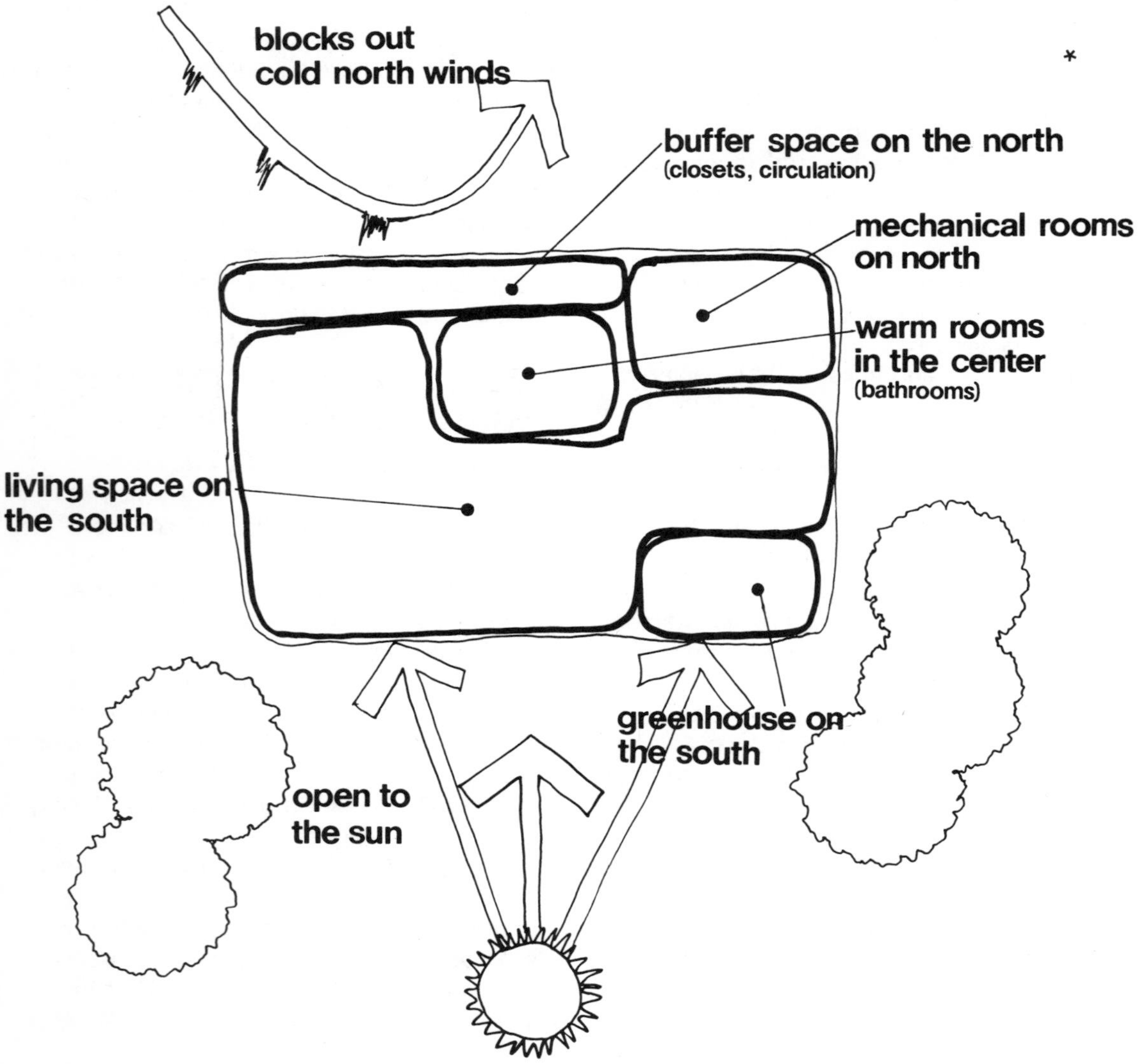

Certain plans (as indicated) have been designed for cluster housing, townhomes, duplexes, or single-family, joined homes with zero-property-line zoning. Thermal conditions and construction cost benefits are improved by joining living units, but daylighting opportunities are usually reduced, fire risks are increased, and sound transmission through walls and floor systems between units must be adequately controlled. (See the "Interiors" section for sound-control methods.)

Open planning is particularly needed in compact homes to avoid a psychologically oppressive interior. Openings between room spaces (open or glazed) provide visual relief in seeing into spaces beyond or an outdoor view. Open planning permits a greater amount of daylight penetration, which conserves energy by reducing artificial illumination. Higher ceiling areas (in contrast to space- and energy-conserving lower ceiling areas) expand our perceptions of space.

blocks out
cold north winds

buffer space on the north
(closets, circulation)

mechanical rooms
on north

warm rooms
in the center
(bathrooms)

living space on
the south

greenhouse on
the south

open to
the sun

Most of the home designs have a high ceiling area. Besides providing psychological relief by opening up living spaces, high ceilings also increase the air volume in a compact home. More oxygen is present and greater air dilution occurs, which can be important for the dispersal of indoor air pollutants caused by chemicals, cooking, smoking, and outgassing of furniture and furnishings.

Open interior planning decreases costly partitions and increases the delight of spaciousness; however, it is counter to privacy and quietness. Acoustics and privacy are probably the most difficult compact home problems. Open planning heightens the probabilities of conflict over the use of televisions, stereos, or musical instruments when there is more than one occupant. Headphones, carpeting, thick wall hangings, and other acoustical absorbers and barriers can reduce the noise problem. Sliding or folding screens (such as in Japanese homes), furniture arrangements, and individual room spaces can increase privacy.

Interior space planning was based on optimal human use and optimal placement of furniture and cabinets. The plans improve interior daylighting by locating windows adjacent to interior walls. Hallways are either eliminated or minimized. Sliding-door closets are used to avoid conflict where interior doors open into rooms. Stacking or side-by-side 24 x 24 inch (61 x 61 centimeter) washers and dryers are shown in most plans. Hot water tanks can be located in storage rooms, lofts, above kitchen or bath ceilings, or in basements when provided.

The plans optimize wall space in bedrooms. Despite tight space, bedrooms have become so important that queen-size beds have been used for most plans. Bedroom spaces can be used for studios, home offices, or playrooms. Loft spaces have been provided for some plans with spiral stairs, ship's ladders, or other means of access. Lofts can be left open or closed, depending on functional use.

Adequate storage space is difficult to provide in compact homes. Storage space for objects, clothes, and other sundry items is frequently inadequate and heightens the probability of loss or damage to small possessions. In these plans, special attention is given to provide useful storage. Storage space and closets are located to act as climatic buffers. Where space permits, kitchen cabinets are shown 30 inches (76 centimeters) deep. In a small kitchen, this greatly increases cabinet and countertop utility and base storage. Storing small, energy-saving appliances on the rear of counters allows for front work space. Bath cabinets also provide storage, although in very small plans, linen closets are omitted. Lack of garage or enclosed-carport storage cabinets raises the question of where to put garden and snow removal equipment, automobile tires, tools, bicycles, and numerous other items. When enough money is available in the home building budget, garages or carports should be included; or as mentioned earlier, provision should be made for their addition at a later date. Including a basement is another way to increase storage capacity. To save construction costs, how space is reduced must be qualified. Kitchens, baths, and utility rooms, with their electrical and mechanical needs and costly cabinet work, are the most expensive spaces within a home. The present preoccupation with multiple baths is counter to affordability, as to both initial and ongoing costs. Thus, reducing the space and elaborations of these areas is most productive in reducing total costs.

To summarize regarding interior planning: The affordable homes presented have task-performance compact-space planning; small-scale space arrangements most efficiently planned for human use; and the use of vertical as well as horizontal space.

Building Envelope. In each home design, the building envelope has a minimal surface-to-interior-volume ratio. This reduces thermal losses at the building's interface with the climate.

Insulation amounts will vary with the climatic location. It is recommended that insulation be tailored to the various external elevations of the building. The roof, because of exposure to the clear sky, the windchill factor, and the fact that the internal heat is greatest at the roof line, will require the most insulation. The north wall in a cold climate would have the next-highest R-factor of insulation, while east, west, and south walls would require less. A lightly insulated south wall, depending on the climate, can be a sensible option. All foundations should be insulated with Styrofoam, and all external walls should have a thermal-insulation sheathing that reduces bridging of wood studs and plates. No insulation with formaldehyde or other material that would dangerously outgas in a fire should be used. Additional information on insulation can be found under "Materials" and in the appendix.

Where conditions permit and fit the budget, a basement can be added. Inasmuch as foundations in a cold climate are apt to be required to depths of 3 feet (.9 meters) extending them down to a total depth of 7 or 8 feet (2.1 to 2.4 meters) will not greatly increase construction costs (if the basement is not finished). This provides cheap future-expansion or present-storage or workshop space. On hillside lots, basement space could become a garage, also.

Upper decks or deck space over adjoining, single or double carports or garages can provide additional, useful outdoor space on a small site. The decks can also be used for outdoor gardening. Many of the designs have a single entry for energy savings and personal security. It is preferentially located to the south or southeast. North entries should be air-locked, but this extra cost is not absolutely essential for south and southeast entries.

Envelope Design. Full, "double-envelope" design is not appropriate to the tight spatial limitations of compact homes. Furthermore, partial-envelope designs and super-insulation are proving to be more economical.[15]

Southside, partial envelopes can be identified as direct gain solar chambers (4 feet [1.2 meters] or less in width), sunspaces, or other forms of architectural enclosures. Ventilated envelopes that capture westside solar radiation and then exhaust the heat to reduce the effects of solar intensity can also be categorized as partial envelopes. Partial envelopes also include roof forms that allow for architecturally contained air passage between the roof and the interior. In hot climates, double-roof construction has been used with an intervening air-flow space that keeps the lower roof and building interior cooler. This is a type of open-ended roof envelope.

Thermal envelopes are particularly suited to secondary solar gain and hybrid system design resolutions. These systems have the advantage of removing (for use and storage) solar-thermal gains from the periphery of the building where heat losses are greatest.

Superinsulation. Insulation of the outer walls and roofs of dwellings is most effective when continuously applied around their exterior surface. This is more economically and practically accomplished for walls than for roofs, although roofs experience greater proportionate (as well as roof-dominant) thermal losses. In the controversy of full double-envelope versus superinsulation construction, analysis has favored superinsulation.[16]

Since compact homes already require a minimized enclosure of insulation, increasing the R-factor of the insulation does not substantially affect total building cost.

An insulation chart in the appendix gives recommended insulation values for various heating zones. These values apply to *standard construction practices* — insulation amounts in superinsulated homes could be much greater. For more information on superinsulated homes, see William Shurcliff's book, *Superinsulated Houses and Double-Envelope Houses.*[16]

Superinsulation incorporates the concept of thermally isolating a home from its climate. A tight, superinsulated home that can discreetly use solar gains along with all other intrinsic, internal heat sources can provide indoor comfort with little or no supplemental heat. Indoor air quality and ventilation are the greatest constraining factors to superinsulated design. In the face of combined indoor and outdoor air pollution, some type of air-quality control system is needed to ensure adequate air quality. Infiltration, thermal bridging, and an effective air/vapor barrier are other considerations within the superinsulation package.

Insulation and the construction designed to accommodate its installation escalate cost. Superinsulation for a compact house with a minimized building enclosure will not be as proportionately great in cost as superinsulating most homes. However, in the interest of long-term affordability, the initial and life-cycle costs for superinsulation should be weighed as economic options. The method and expense for ventilating and air-quality control should also be included as cost considerations.

Superinsulation can ignore or limit certain factors, including the relationship of the occupant to the external climate, optimization of daylighting, expansion to usable outdoor space, external views, climatic design factors, and the architectural aesthetic. The steady-state thermal isolation counters the vitality of human metabolism and psychoneural behavior.

Design criteria for superinsulated houses have been developed by Professor Howard Faulkner at the University of Southern Maine.[17] According to these criteria, minimum insulation levels should be as follows:

Above-grade exterior walls	R-35
Ceiling	R-55
Floor w/out heat below	R-20

[15]Hank Huber, "A Step Beyond the Envelope House," *Solar Age,* vol. 7, no. 6, June 1982, p. 24.

[16]William A. Shurcliff, *Superinsulated Houses and Double-Envelope Houses: A Preliminary Survey of Principles and Practice* (Cambridge, Mass.: William A. Shurcliff, 1980).

[17]"Superinsulation: Current Status and Future Trends," *Energy Design Update,* (Boston: Cahners Publishing Company, 1984) p. 1.

Exterior foundation wall to grade	R-20
Exterior foundation wall below grade	R-10
Foundation interior	R-20

More commonly, the following insulation levels are used:

Above-grade exterior walls	R-40+
Ceiling	R-60+
Floor w/out heat below	R-30
Exterior foundation wall to grade	R-30
Exterior foundation wall below grade	R-20
Foundation interior	R-30+

Our national, state, and localized utility networks are very fragile and face increasing probabilities of failure, sabotage, or interruption. The 300 to 900 square foot (27.9 to 83.6 square meter) homes in this book are ideally suited to be attached to existing dwellings as complete, superinsulated units into which all of the home dwellers can retreat under a power outage. A supplemental heating system and other supplemental provisions for food, cooking, food preservation, water, sleeping gear, communication, and toilet needs should be supplied. Such a facility can be designed as a measure against nuclear fallout, hurricanes, tornadoes, or other natural disasters.

Exterior Surface. With regard to durable exterior surface materials, Sto, Settef, or Dryvit, which are acrylic materials applied by trowel or sprayed onto a nylon mesh that covers polystyrene insulation board, offer the advantage of continuous insulation over the exterior of wood, concrete, or masonry construction. It is a literally unbroken insulation wrap that isolates the structure of the building from the climate.

Other exterior surface materials that may be used include rough-sawn vertical, horizontal, or diagonal exterior plywood or metal siding; wood shakes; or pressed wood. Finish colors should match climatic profiles (see climatic color chart). Exterior siding should fit tightly to avoid air infiltration and be insulated from the frame of the building. Materials that are economical, durable, and relatively maintenance free are preferred for exterior surfaces.

Daylighting and Shading. Daylighting is a very important function. Daylight reaching a site and building has three sources: direct sunlight, skylight (skyvault irradiance), and reflected light from the ground and adjacent objects and buildings. Design can use the more uniform ambience of skylight with relatively little control, whereas considerable control is needed over direct, transient sunlight streaming into a building. These small home designs employ daylighting as much as possible to reduce the need for artificial lighting. When it is required, artificial lighting should be minimized and be located and selected to conform to task-performance needs. Good light output and light color with minimal electrical demand are selection criteria for artificial lighting fixtures and lamps. More information about optimizing and controlling daylight can be found in the "Interiors" section.

Shading is critical to passive solar optimization. Roof overhangs or canopies are a very important design element that not only control the shading of windows but also reduce the solar-thermal impact on exterior walls. Roof overhangs can be extended to form the roof of a carport, patio, or porch. Overhangs also offer peripheral protection from rain, snow, and wind for the architecture and for persons entering, walking, or conducting outdoor activities under protective cover. Slotted or slatted portions of roof overhangs can aid convective air flows around the building as well as internal ventilation through nearby vent and window openings. Ventilation space between an exterior shading device and the building should be provided to allow for hot air to escape.

Each compass exposure — north, south, east, or west — along with the latitude and climate, should be considered in residential design. The southern exposure is the most critical for passive solar heating during the winter months. Shading devices for south-facing passive systems require careful calculation to avoid any winter coverage of south glazing and to allow for complete summer shading.

An external shading device is more effective than an internal one, since it blocks the sun's heat before it can pass through the glazing. With fixed overhangs, an architectural compromise must always be made between optimized passive solar gains and desirable seasonal shading. For south glazing, a fixed overhang that blocks sun of September 21 will also shade the window on March 21 when solar gains may be desirable.

An adjustable external device, such as retractable awning, would be most effective, especially in spring and fall. Overhangs with adjustable slats or louvers can also respond to seasonal solar-positional change, as can deciduous vegetation. Trees, hanging or trailing vines, shrubs, or other deciduous shading can more closely match solar seasons and positions. Leaf-out and leaf-drop times and density (branch structure, leaf size) should be considered when choosing appropriate vegetation. Vines can be grown over trellises, grillwork, or arbors attached or close to exterior walls of the home or over roof areas. Entire walls can likewise be cooled with vegetation. (Remember that bugs accompany plants.) Vegetation also cools by transpiration and moisture.

The sun's altitude angles should always be plotted on a scaled, sectional drawing of the building to determine the diurnal and seasonal effect, direction, and intensity of solar radiation. From a plan view (overhead looking down), the most useful solar radiation in the northern hemisphere for winter heating (November, December, January, February) lies within a 120-degree-angled, due-south gradient.

Shading for east windows is sometimes needed, especially in warm and hot climates. Morning sun from the east can be enjoyable in winter but becomes more of a problem in summer. Overhangs are effective for summer shading of east windows. West, afternoon solar radiation entering interior spaces from low-angled, afternoon, western sun, usually coinciding with the hottest daily air temperatures, is a problem in almost all climates. A combination of westside roof overhangs and architectural projections (fin walls) can shade west windows to a large degree. Awnings or other shading materials vertically attached to the edge of the overhang are most effective for either total interception or partial, filtered attenuation of the sun's rays.

Northside windows can suffer some undesirable intrusion in summer from the west, setting sun. The author has used vertical fins to the west of north windows to intercept low-angled, late-in-the-day sunlight and also to increase early-morning daylighting to northside interior spaces. East and west shading is not really a major problem in residences because the glass area can be greatly reduced and heat-absorbing and

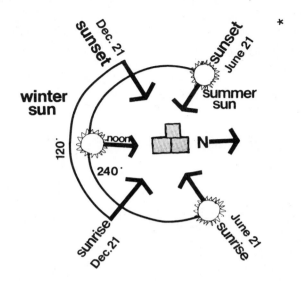

reflective glass on the east and west, respectively, can be used. South glass areas are most important.

Sunspaces themselves can act as a shading device for a home, so no shading is shown in the plan, perspective, and section drawings. However, if the sunspace is used as a habitable space, shading would be needed, even though this might cut performance somewhat.

In general design, broad overhangs are more indicated for hot, southern regions. In northern regions, the need for admitting maximum sunlight predominates; clean building envelopes with flush roof-wall treatments should be used to optimize solar gains. This strategy can cause some late-summer or early-fall (August 15 to September 30) overheating in certain areas.

A light-colored reflective surface for an overhang underside will bring more light and more thermal gains into a space. A darker color underneath improves the view to the outside by lessening visual disturbance. It acts as an eyeshade, improving visual adaptation, giving less glare and more comfort.

In hot-arid regions, entire or partial slotted-roof areas can act as a pleasant climate-moderating influence upon the architecture and provide useful outdoor shade for human relaxation and activities. In warm and hot climates, entire attached-lath houses can provide shade for gatherings, plants, and animals; they should not interfere with planned passive solar systems.

Attics and Crawl Spaces. The author has avoided the use of conventional unusable space that usually relies on trusses. Such attic spaces are required to be vented by code. Cold-weather attic ventilation as well as ventilation of underfloor crawl spaces can, without meticulous construction and insulation, cause undesirable heat losses. Common ceiling and roof joists, even though well insulated, possess the usual cold-weather disadvantages of conductive heat loss through thermal bridging. This applies to common-floor crawl-space joists and exterior walls unless continuous insulation extends over the exterior supportive studs. In all cases, insulation for climatic protection from cold or hot temperatures should be an outer membrane.

Plumbing. Plumbing work requires knowledge, experience, and, usually, a license. All of the plans have been designed to economically integrate the plumbing of kitchens, baths, and laundry facilities, whether on one or two levels. Not only will less labor and material be required to install the plumbing lines, but it will perform more efficiently with less energy loss. The water heater, combined with a preheat tank served by a drain-back or other kind of fluid-type, solar water heating system, should be located as close as possible to the plumbing fixtures. With proper structural support, tanks can be located above, below, or where space can be made available on the main-floor level. Flow-restricting faucets should be used as well as water-saving toilets. Instant-flow water heating elements that avoid a water heating tank can perform well with a solar preheat tank. It is more economical to install a conventional tub with a shower than to provide a shower stall and a separate tub.

It is important that a plumbing contractor's estimate be based on the minimal materials and labor required by the conceptual layout, rather than a plumbing-fixture unit basis. Plumbing fixtures vary greatly in cost, so compare them.

Electrical. Electrical work also requires knowledge, experience, and, usually, a license. The compact plans require minimal wiring distribution. Most residential lighting fixtures and lamps are inefficient in providing useful light. Ordinary porcelain or metal-plated sockets with G-type lamps give good light and are inexpensive lighting solutions for over bathroom sinks (ceiling or sidewall), ceilings in front of sliding-door closets, halls, stairways, and storage spaces. Very small kitchens can use this solution, but a shallow, surface-mounted, shielded, fluorescent light can be used for larger kitchens. The electrical estimate should be based on the minimal material and labor required to wire these compact homes, rather than a per-outlet basis. Always make adequate allowance for ease in electrical wiring. Select the most energy-conserving appliances, equipment, and devices. Compare "Energyguide" labels to determine yearly operating costs. New energy-efficient light bulbs, such as incandescent bulbs with krypton gas or fluorescent lamps that fit incandescent fixtures, will save money in the long run.

In underground or earth-sheltered housing or when concrete or masonry walls are to be left exposed, electrical work must be planned to accommodate outlet boxes and wiring. Metal conduits can go under the floor with enclosed outlet boxes sitting on the floor.

Passive Solar Energy and Passive Solar Strategies

The plan, form, scale, and orientation of every dwelling make it more or less effective as a collector, retainer, and distributor of thermal energy received directly and indirectly from the sun. A primary concern is how to design a home to optimally respond to and use solar radiation for heating, ventilating, air tempering, and cooling with little or no mechanical assistance. A strictly "passive" solar system uses no mechanical or electrical assistance, relying upon natural energy flows (conduction, convection, radiation) to collect and transport heat and control air movement.

Passive solar heating systems require unobstructed solar exposures. If winter sunlight does not directly pass into lower-level or main-level interior spaces as desired, an upper story or the roof can become the solar-energy-collecting area for a passive or hybrid system. Using passive solar energy through all seasons of the year for inductive ventilation and cooling rather than only for winter heating is functionally and economically beneficial.

The use of space on a daily as well as seasonal basis should determine the type of passive solar strategies used for each designated area. The most appropriate, seasonal, passive solar strategies relate principally to climatic space planning and the detailing of architectural form and apertures.

As the size of a residence increases (usually greater than 1000 square feet [92.9 square meters]), centralization of energy becomes more appropriate and the specific differentiation of passive solar systems according to the nature of interior-space use becomes more effective in cost and function. A combination of passive subsystems can increase overall efficiency and flexibility and be more practical as interior-space volume increases.

Solar Components and Systems

The following descriptions cover the major passive and hybrid solar components and systems used in the compact, solar home designs. These systems represent affordable options suitable for use in these homes. These descriptions of the major system types will serve as reference when data on the individual plans and designs are reviewed.

Thermal Mass Floor. A thermal mass floor can function as a thermal storage component of a direct gain solar system. Solar radiation entering the space through south-facing glazing (usually clear, double-paned glass) directly strikes the floor. The effect of the solar intensity depends upon the angle of incidence: Perpendicular radiation produces the greatest intensity. However, over 90 percent of the direct solar radiation will still be intercepted by a surface facing up to 25 degrees from the perpendicular to the sun.[18] Diffuse solar radiation also enters through the glazing along with direct sunlight. Both can be intercepted and stored by the thermal mass floor.

When solar radiation strikes the surface of a floor, it is either reflected or absorbed.[19] (The floor is usually an opaque material, so no solar radiation is transmitted.) Reflection of solar radiation is basically related to the color of a surface, since the color of an object is the visible radiation reflected from it. A black color occurs as most of the

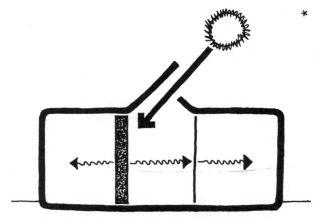

section/centralization of energy

incident visible radiation is being absorbed; a white color results when most of the radiation is being reflected. White represents a combination of all spectral colors that make up the various wavelengths of visible radiation. A thermal mass floor should be a dark color to maximize solar absorption.

The incident solar radiation (electromagnetic shortwave radiation) absorbed by a floor is converted into longwave, thermal energy (heat). The absorbed solar radiation excites the surface molecules of the floor, increasing their rate of vibrational movement, which, in turn, increases the heat deeper within the floor material.[20] This thermal energy is distributed, or transferred, throughout the floor by conduction; that is, heat will flow from warmer to cooler molecules of a substance that are in direct contact with each other. Eventually, the ma-

terial acquires a more uniform temperature through the conduction process, as heat is conducted from the surface of the material and stored within its interior.[21]

Heat is also transferred from the floor by convection to the surrounding air and by radiation to adjacent, cooler objects. A thermal mass floor provides thermal energy storage for direct solar gains. Several different materials can be used for a mass floor. The most common are masonry materials such as concrete, brick or stone. Thickened concrete (6 inches [15 centimeters] is a prescribed, effective thickness) can be hand troweled or have a small, aggregate finish. The concrete can then be stained or painted with a dull, dark, floor finish (for the lowest cost) or be topped with full-depth brick, dark pavers, or various forms of ceramic or concrete tile. The tile can be unglazed or mat glazed, but not glossy.

[18]Edward Mazria, *The Passive-Solar Energy Book: Expanded Professional Edition* (Emmaus, Pa.: Rodale Press, 1979), p. 14.

[19]Ibid., p. 15.

[20]Ibid., p. 20

[21]Ibid., pp. 21-27.

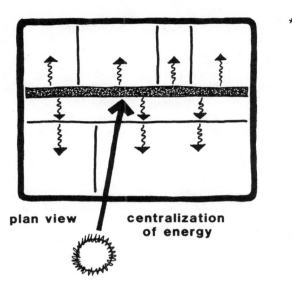

*

plan view   centralization of energy

Another possibility is constructing the floor of dark brick set edgewise into a sand bed.

Mass floors should not be covered by rugs or carpeting. Furniture and furnishings placement is very important. Care should be taken so that furniture will cast minimal shadows, be reflective to the floor, or not physically block the path of sunlight reaching the floor.

Economic advantages that make a concrete mass floor a most affordable solar-storage option are: no in-depth forming is required; there is only one surface to finish; and, the floor is uniformly supported by the earth, requiring no special structural support (as opposed to a mass wall or large volume of water) unless it intervenes between floors.

Thermal Mass Bunkers. Also part of a direct gain system, a thermal mass bunker consists of thermal storage materials placed in a clear-plastic or glass-covered cabinet with appropriate ventilation slots or a selec-tive-surface or direct-thermal-exchange unit near south-facing glazing to intercept direct solar radiation. Thermal storage can be provided by containers of water or eutectic salts. Water can be stored in small containers, such as plastic or glass jars or bottles, and be placed on racks or shelves. The water can be colored dark and should contain an agent to retard algae growth, such as copper sulfate or chlorine. Adequate structural support for the weight of the water must also be provided. (One gallon [3.8 liters] of water weighs approximately 8 pounds [3.6 kilograms]).

Eutectic salts, or phase-change materials (PCM), are low-temperature-melting-point salts that absorb heat as they melt and release this heat when they resolidify (changing phase from solid to liquid to solid). The salts can be contained in cans, bags, or tubes. Partial resolidification after many cycles has been a problem with eutectic salts, and some of the salts are corrosive, causing difficulties in maintaining the integrity of container seals to prevent leakage. Manufacturers claim these problems have been solved.

Water and salt containers can be faced with a selective surface to increase thermal performance. A selective surface is an absorber coating, such as black chrome, that has a high percentage of solar aborptance but emits very little thermal radiation — much less than ordinary black surfaces at the same temperature.[22] This reduces re-radiant heat loss.

Eutectic salts and water have a higher heat capacity per unit volume than masonry materials, so that a smaller volume of material can be used to achieve equal storage performance. An added advantage is that floors can be carpeted and furniture placed up to the edge of the thermal storage container, allowing more flexible use of floor space; plus, the movability and light weight of eutectic salts (or empty water containers) also increases flexibility. A corrolary system similar to a thermal mass bunker is water storage in large drums or fiberglass tubes. These units can be disguised by a structural framework to give the appearance of a piece of furniture; for example, a window seat or a freestanding wall can be set within concrete or masonry, particularly with the end of metal containers directly exposed to the sun.

Sunspace with Thermal Mass Floor and/or Wall or Thermal Bunker. Integral, vertically glazed sunspaces are featured in many of the compact home designs. These

---

[22]Bruce Anderson, *The Solar Home Book: Heating, Cooling, and Designing with the Sun* (Harrisville, N.H.: Cheshire Books, 1976), p. 158.

spaces can be used simply as a pleasant, sunny living space, with or without furniture, or as a greenhouse for growing plants and food. Most of the sunspaces have vertical glazing, as opposed to sloped glass, for several reasons: vertical glazing is easier and less expensive to install; it collects less dirt and is easier to maintain; problems with seasonal overheating, energy losses, and leakage are greatly reduced; sun-control devices and movable insulation can be installed more easily; many glass manufacturers will not warrant their units in sloped installations; some building codes require laminated glass for sloping installations.

The most economic glazing for sunspaces is fixed, tempered (as usually required by code), double-paned, insulative, clear glass in standard, patio-door replacement sizes. Greenhouses can be glazed with clear, double-wall, extruded acrylic, which is light-diffusing and can help reduce plant scalding. Thermal-break sash systems should also be used with plastic glazing. In some of the plans, the sunspaces are fitted with side-sliding, double-glazed, patio doors. These wood, metal, or vinyl doors should be designed to avoid thermal bridging and have foot locks for secure, positional ventilation.

Inner glazing for sunspaces can be single-glazed patio doors that do not need thermal-break frames. Inner glazing provides useful secondary daylighting and secondary thermal gains to interior spaces and allows occupant control of heat flow from the sunspace.

The sunspaces are designed to use concrete floors, tiled concrete masonry, water tubes, drums, or thermal bunkers for passive-thermal storage. Thermal mass walls, placed on the north, east, or west, are another storage option but are more expensive.

The sunspace can become a hybrid solar system (a passive system requiring mechanical assistance) when heat from direct solar gains is mechanically drawn off (usually by a fan) and channeled to some type of remote storage. This could be a gravel-filled, underfloor plenum; a vertical-cavity, thermal mass wall; rock bin; or water tank (using an air-to-water heat exchanger). The heat can then be stored and retrieved for later use, in phase with time-period need.

Clerestory Duct System. This system functions as a hybrid solar component. A south-facing clerestory admits direct solar gains to a black, lateral, round duct suspended behind it. The clerestory can have an overhead reflector, which will increase winter solar gains, reducing the need for a larger glass area because of solar concentration. Less glass results in less high-level, warm-air heat loss. The reflector should be designed to shade the clerestory in summer. Under most climatic conditions, the solar cutoff should be aligned with the equinox.

Solar-heated air in the duct is destratified by using a solar-powered (photovoltaic) or electrically driven fan, with the air being moved to remote thermal storage (as described above). Destratification is a major technique to make use of the hot, high-level strata of interior air at a ceiling by either distributing it throughout for temperature equalization or delivering it to thermal storage (along with more intense, direct solar gains).

Internal Thermal Wall. The internal thermal wall can be a component of a direct gain or hybrid system. The wall can be located in a central area of the house or be on the north side. A clerestory with a reflector can be used to supply direct solar gains to a water wall or masonry wall constructed of brick, block, stone, adobe, or precast or poured-in-place concrete. A centralized location within the interior allows the wall to radiate heat outward to all surrounding areas. A northside location can serve the northside interior spaces. Another possible configuration is a thermal mass cavity wall, filled with gravel as a storage medium. Solar-heated air or other internally heated air can be delivered to the wall by a thermocontrolled, insulated duct-and-blower system, making it a hybrid system. Slots on the bottom of the wall would provide for return air.

The sizing of the mass-to-glass and other passive system considerations should be performed by an architect, engineer, or designer familiar with passive solar design and thermal storage requirements. Rough sizing guidelines can be found in Mazria's *The Passive Solar Energy Book* (see references), along with recommended wall thicknesses and other information.

Partial, Southside, Thermal Envelope. The components in this passive system form a direct gain/hybrid combination. The major element is a south-facing, solar, hot-air envelope that is constructed using two, parallel, glazed walls. The outer layer of glazing should be clear glass in single- or double-paned units. The inner glazing layer is heat-absorbing glass or plastic or a dark intervening vertical or horizontal blind (reflective on one side against summer solar radiation). These two glazing layers form a sandwich or a cavity that traps direct solar gains. The solar-heated air in the envelope

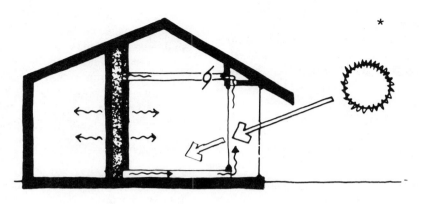

solar entrapment with dark heat-absorbing glazing/storage in vertical central thermal mass/secondary thermal gains

is delivered to remote storage, which could be a central, interior, rock bin or an under-floor, gravel plenum.

Thermal Attic. Most of the homes in this book do not have conventional attics for the heat loss and economic reasons explained earlier. However, with proper design and careful construction, an attic can be used for storage, mechanical equipment, or as a passive energy system.

A thermal attic could be part of a direct gain or hybrid system with mass storage in the attic space or remote storage elsewhere in the home. The advantage of a thermal attic is that it can provide access to the sun if solar access to the exterior south wall is obstructed. Peripheral house walls can be freed up for other functions, if desired. Also, thermal mass placed in an attic can be spread horizontally for more uniform structural loading. Having the passive system in the attic separates it from the rest of the house, so occupants are not exposed to

direct energy impacts. Note, however, that in colder climates movable insulation may be required at night to prevent heat loss from the attic.

Trombe Wall. A trombe wall forms part of a direct gain solar system. In general, a trombe wall is constructed of concrete (which can be poured-in-place, solid blocks, or hollow blocks filled with concrete), usually 12 inches (30 centimeters) thick. Glazing is placed 3 to 4 inches (7.6 to 10.2 centimeters) in front of the wall, covering the entire concrete area. Brick, stone, or adobe could also be used for wall materials. Only one home design in this book uses a trombe wall because, in most cases, the disadvantages of a trombe wall outweigh the advantages.

Construction of concrete and masonry walls is expensive, and if they serve a structural function reinforcement is necessary, which adds to cost. The weight of the wall requires substantial footings and foun-

dations. Daylighting and view are eliminated, unless openings in the wall are provided — which, again, increase costs. Vents installed in the wall for thermosiphoning air circulation can also add to the expense and the upper vents require backdraft dampers to prevent reverse air circulation at night. Reradiant heat loss through the glazing at night is also a problem unless movable insulation is placed between the glazing and the wall, or outside, over the glazing surface. Finishing the interior wall surface for appearance, although not absolutely necessary, is another price-ticket item. The thickness of the wall uses up living space. A trombe wall stores solar gains near the periphery of the house, whereas centralized storage decreases losses and will allow heat to migrate to surrounding spaces.

A trombe wall provides heat storage, solar collection, and heat distribution in one unit. Room spaces are served by solar-driven, air-convection heating and by thermal-lag, radiant heating. Security from break-in is improved. A trombe wall can work well in spaces where daylight and view are not needed, such as in bedrooms. A mass wall of this type needs very little maintenance, and use of patterned, diffusing-type solar glazing will obscure the view of the wall materials, offering improved appearance and greater materials flexibility. A trombe wall can be an aid to summer cooling, if vented at the top to the outside, by augmenting stack-effect (inductive) airflow of cool, outdoor air.

Active Solar Systems. Active solar collection systems for year-round heating of domestic hot water, hot spa tubs, and, possibly, spot zones such as bathrooms or inner entry halls can be either liquid or air type. Air-type collectors require air-to-water heat exchangers and avoid freezing problems but increase probabilities of higher electrical supportive load demand. Drainback water collectors with low-iron or iron-free glazing have a high cost-benefit ratio. Check the specifications, performance test data, in-place costs, the credibility of the solar company, operational efficiency, and maintenance durability of the system.

To help compare solar collector performance, look for the Solar Rating and Certification Corporation (SRCC) rating label. The SRCC certifies and rates collectors tested by accredited labs. The labels give collector output in Btus under various conditions. This rating can be divided by the cost of the collector to get a Btu-per-dollar figure that can be used to compare with other SRCC-rated collectors.[23] The Florida Solar Energy Center also conducts a certification program.[24] Note: To obtain the SRCC ratings contact your state energy office or write to Solar Rating and Certification Corporation, 1001 Connecticut Avenue, NW, Suite 800, Washington DC 20036. Ask for information about the *Directory of SRCC-Certified Solar Collector Ratings.* Yearly subscriptions are available.

The Florida Solar Energy Center has rated 372 collector models manufactured by 135 companies (Florida Solar Energy Center, 300 State Road 401, Cape Canaveral, FL 32920).

Many collector companies are now offering complete domestic hot water solar heating systems, including collectors, storage tank, pump, and controls. The SRCC has begun rating these packaged systems; results are now available. For heating domestic hot water, collectors should face due south or within 20 degrees of due south and be mounted at an angle of latitude plus 5 degrees (approximately). For winter space heating, the collectors should be mounted at an angle of latitude plus 15 degrees.

Active systems can use air or liquids as the fluids for transferring solar energy to interior use or thermal storage. Storage can be gravel, water, masonry, concrete, or eutectic salts (phase-change materials). Active collectors are likely to have a single low-iron glass cover, selective-surface coating on the absorber plate, and an insulated edging and backing. Nonselective coatings may be used with double-glazed covers for very cold climates. The number of collectors and amount of storage needed should be sized by calculation. These determinations can be made by an architect, designer, solar engineer, or by reference to various books.

Types of active solar systems include water (open- or closed-loop) drain-back systems; water drain-down systems; antifreeze-loop systems; silicone oil-loop systems; and, air-type collector systems. High-density site development as well as the usually congested housing of existing neighborhoods often precludes effective use of south-wall passive solar designs. In such cases roof area may be the only exposure open to the south winter sun. If solar domestic water heating has already been decided upon, adding a few additional panels to provide cold-weather space heating can be the best economic option. Initial and life-cycle cost comparisons should be made between direct gain clerestory, hybrid, and active solar roof systems.

Hybrid Solar Systems. Hybrid solar systems use blowers, fans, or other mechanical devices to transfer and/or distribute heat from solar radiation. A principal advantage of hybrid systems is that they can relocate solar-thermal gains to storage or to the most advantageous place in the building interior. This "advantageous place" is usually at the lowest level of a home, as in a basement or insulated thermal storage under the main- or lower-level floor of the living space. Remote thermal storage can be more efficient and provide more effective time-frame use of solar heat with hybrid (or active) systems.

Cooling, ventilation, air tempering, humidification, and air distribution can also be more easily accomplished with powered (hybrid) systems. Air tempering is when cool or cold outdoor air is warmed (preferably by solar energy) as it is brought into the interior. Filtration can be especially important during winter months when outdoor air inversions can increase atmospheric pollution. Humidification that improves winter, indoor-heating comfort can also be a solar function by water evaporation. Destratification should not be forgotten as part of internal energy distribution. A hybrid system can be either an independent destratification system or be part of a larger air distribution network.

Mechanical Systems and Supplemental Heating

Ducting should be provided as required; however, except for the larger, space-efficient plans, no regular mechanical heating

[23]Stuart Diamond, "Energy Products: Don't Get Ripped Off," *New Shelter,* vol. 3, no. 9, Nov.-Dec. 1982, p. 59.

[24]Ibid.

system should be needed besides the remote storage of solar energy for its distribution. For housing units that might use a central, forced-air or hydronic heating system, pulse-combustion (requiring no flue), or other gas-fired, energy-conserving furnace units can be installed. Some operate with concentric side wall flues that take in fresh combustion air heated by the outgoing gases. Their high efficiency can range from about 80 to 95 percent. These systems can operate on natural gas or LPG (propane). The greater question is what to use as a backup for the passive solar capabilities of the building.

Although natural gas is generally a less expensive fuel for heating a conventional house, this may not apply to a passive solar, compact dwelling. Its small scale, reduced interior volume, close proximity of the occupants to the heating element, and larger coefficient of internal load (i.e., people, lights, cooking, refrigeration, and other equipment) can decrease winter heating needs. The solar fraction has a direct bearing on supplemental heating demand.

Since standard, central heating systems are not necessary for most of the compact homes, the most economical and practical choice for backup heat is likely to be electrical. Electric, hydronic (fluid-contained) radiators or baseboard heaters are suggested, with separate wall thermostats for each room to permit "mini" thermal zoning of interior spaces. Conventional electric-resistance heaters with exposed elements are not recommended because they ground out beneficial negative ions that usually occur in the atmosphere. Complete radiant floor systems are not advisable because they deteriorate leg muscles. However, radiant ceiling systems or wall panels are recom-

mended and should have separate room thermostats.

Unvented kerosene space heaters, a popular method of supplemental zone heating, are not recommended. They are banned in some states and cities because of the potential fire hazard. A more serious problem is the indoor oxygen depletion and air contamination. However, newer models that vent to the outdoors and use outdoor air for combustion are recommended as a practical, low-cost source of supplemental heat. A major advantage in using hydronic, radiant-baseboard units or through-the-wall kerosene systems for supplemental heating in these compact homes is the elimination of the space needed for mechanical equipment and ducting.

Problems similar to those for unvented kerosene heaters exist with wood-burning stoves and fireplaces. Only the emotional attachment to a blazing hearth gives the fireplace any validity as a heating system. Most people realize that fireplaces are notorious energy-losers. Most of the heat they produce escapes up the chimney, along with already-heated room air. Wood stoves are more efficient, but they share with fireplaces and unvented kerosene heaters the serious problems of indoor air pollution and oxygen depletion (unless supplied with outdoor combustion air and fresh-air replenishment). Combustion by-products from these devices include carbon monoxide, hydrogen cyanide, nitrogen dioxide, sulfate, and various respirable particles.[25] Also, wood-burning equipment causes outdoor air pollution that can pollute an entire neighborhood or community (although catalytic stoves

are purportedly much more efficient than other types of equipment and reduce emission and creosote problems). Burning wood

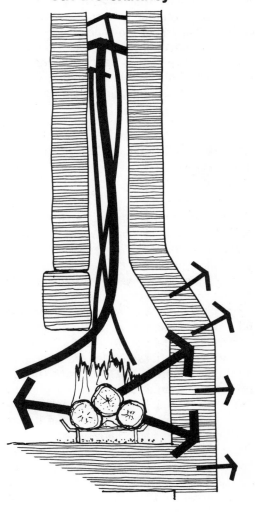

fireplace loses heat through back and out the chimney *

---

[25]Michael Lafavore, "Clean Air Indoors," *New Shelter,* vol. 3, no. 5, May-June 1982, p. 22.

or other solid fuels for space heating is not reasonably justifiable, given the serious problems involved; therefore, the plans presented are not designed for either stoves or fireplaces (although, in some designs, such additions are possible). The use of stoves should principally be for *emergency* heating and cooking. Fireplaces are a non-affordable luxury that have no place in a high-density community because of their air pollution. They cost too much and occupy too large a space for an affordable, compact home. In climates that need seasonal air-conditioning but have mild winters, water-to-air or air-to-air heat pumps are appropriate.

A Few Words About Garages

In low-cost housing, garages would not be provided — just parking spaces. Carports put a car in shadow so it is less conspicuous, but they do not eliminate the appearance problem or conceal stored items. A closed garage can neatly hide the vehicle plus the rest of the visual mess.

A small house with a single-car garage and a small house with a double-car garage are different matters of proportion. The larger the garage and garage door are in proportion to the house, the more the house appears to be an attachment — especially a compact house. It is very difficult to disguise a large garage door to make it less conspicuous — particularly when cost is critical. One way is with color. Light colors should be avoided. A muted, medium-to-dark gray or neutral tone tends to recede from the eye and would reduce a garage door's predominance. Less contrast between the house color and the garage door color will help make the garage door less noticeable. Painting the house a lighter color than the garage door will also make the garage door less conspicuous and the house appear larger. Building room or loft spaces over the garage door can make it blend in more with the total architecture.

When new developments have no alleys (because they are too expensive), a direct drive from the street to the garage is the most practical and least costly option. Setting the garage back from the street enough for a car to park allows extra, temporary parking space for guests and visitors.

Security in urban areas is a major problem. An attached garage with an automatic door opener and direct, inside access to the house solves some of this problem. Garages protect people as well as the vehicle, its contents, and other valuable items, such as bicycles, lawnmowers, etc.

An attached garage also has the advantage of acting as a climatic buffer between the cold outdoor climate and the house. To be most effective, the garage should be located on the north or northwest sides of the house if possible, to block prevailing winter winds from these directions. The optimal configuration for cold climates is a garage attached to the north side of the house with an east-facing door. In all climates, garages provide shelter for a vehicle, protecting it from climatic impacts, theft, and vandalism. In cold climates, the avoidance of snow and ice on the vehicle, protection of the finish, and the comfort of getting into a warmer vehicle on cold morning are added inducements for a garage. Warmup time and consequent fuel consumption is reduced, adding to affordability.

A garage is an economic problem. Although it costs much less than finished interior space, in low-cost housing a garage is the optional construction item most frequently eliminated. For most of the designs in this book, an attached garage is possible, hopefully included during the initial construction or added at a later date.

Don't overlook the fact that a garage (depending on the exposure) can be a major solar obstruction in passive solar home design. The shortest access to a street or alley has much to do with practicality, convenience, maintenance, and affordability. On a narrow site where a garage must be located between the house (facing south) and a street or alley, the garage (or carport) becomes a formidable obstacle to south-wall, passive solar use. One solution is to design the garage itself as a passive-hybrid or active solar system serving the living space. Another design alternative is to simply place the living unit above the garage with direct access to the living area. Many of the designs in the book are based on a 20 x 20 foot (6.1 x 6.1 meter) or 24 x 24 foot (7.3 x 7.3 meter) square plan, the size of a double-car garage. In temperate or cold climates, continuous insulation between the garage and house interior is a must to avoid thermal bridging. Heat from the car or cars will also heat the garage space and tend to reduce heat loss from a floor above.

From a community development standpoint, garages eliminate the eyesore resulting from many vehicles crowded into large, common- or individual-site parking areas. Large-scale common parking will dominate the climate-moderation and aesthetic advantage of landscaping.

Cross Ventilation and Inductive Air Flow

Cross ventilation is most effective as a diagonal function of interior space. The *Uniform Building Code* requirement of openable exterior openings with an area not less than one-twentieth of the total floor area[26] might be reasonable for a room that is closed with no other opening that vents to the outside. When there is an inlet for outdoor air and an outlet, with the inlet as low and the outlet as high as possible within one room space (preferably diagonal or as far apart as possible from each other), warm air will rise and exhaust to the outside as cooler air enters to replace it. This concept of ventilating by temperature differences rather than using the force of outdoor wind motion is known as inductive convection. Inductive ventilation can be accelerated by using solar chimneys or plenums heated by late-in-the-day thermal radiation to create a greater temperature differential.

The "stack effect" depends on temperature differential, the height between inlet and outlet, and the size of the apertures. The 1977 ASHRAE *Handbook of Fundamentals* gives an equation for determining airflow caused by stack effect.[27] This equation can be used to determine inlet and outlet sizes if the desired airflow rate is known. Recommended ventilation levels in the ASHRAE handbook for residences are 7-10 cubic feet per minute (cfm) per person in general living areas and 30-50 cfm per person in kitchens and bathrooms. It is

[26]Uniform Building Code, p. 63.

[27]American Society of Heating, Refrigeration, and Air-conditioning Engineers, *Handbook of Fundamentals* (New York: ASHRAE; 1977), pp. 21.11, 21.12.

plan view

intake air

expelled air

solar radiation provides daylight and acts as a driving force to inductively convect interior air

likely (with clean air conditions) that these levels could be lower (such as 3 to 7½ cfm per person) in these small, affordable homes. However, if smoking is allowed or other pollutants are present, ventilation requirements should be much higher.

Cross ventilation with diagonal air movement can effectively use wind motion. Such direct-wind, nighttime flushing or daytime ventilation is most appropriate to hot-humid areas. In drier climates where nights are cooler, inductive ventilation is particularly effective. Independent, screened intake vents or screened, outside louvered doors are generally more effective than using operable windows placed for view or daylighting. Such vents can be most appropriately located as air intakes to maximize cross ventilation in coordination with manually or mechanically operated exhaust vents.

Not only is cross ventilation a basic concept for effective room ventilation, but it also applies to the entire interior air volume of the home. The position of interior doorways and other openings (such as those through stairways) and interior light wells is critical to whole-house ventilation.

The house should be viewed as a complete system of corridors, rooms, doorways, and other openings that allows natural convective airflow to cool and ventilate the building. As direct sunlight enters, a building acts as a natural convective-heat pump. Interior air rises more rapidly as the sun's radiant energy increases interior thermal gains. Cooler masses of interior air move across the floor to displace the rising, solar-heated air. With the building performing as a cross-ventilating duct system, the solar gains can be exhausted with the assistance of the solar heat-pump effect. This produces a hot-weather advantage by providing comfortable, cooler, stratified air near the floor and also affords the best opportunity for high-level roof venting. In winter or other periods when interior heating is desired, a motorized destratification fan should be used to bring high, ceiling-level, warm air down to the floor of the living space, under the floor, or into a thermal storage medium such as gravel, masonry, concrete, water, or eutectic salts for longer-period heat retention.

Lower peripheral interior ceilings adjoining either centralized or other appropriate, high-ceilinged-room spaces cause interior air to naturally convect to the high ceiling space where it is more easily recoverable for interior destratification. As solar-photovoltaic and direct-current-matched fan motors become economically available, they can be used for destratification.

Outdoor-air intakes that pass through the earth, earth berms, or heat-exchange, subsurface air wells will cool incoming air in summer and warm it in winter by the earth's temperature. If you live in an area with high automobile traffic, the highest possible roof air intake will provide a lower amount of polluted air; in a hot-humid area water vapor in moist air drawn through earth tubes will condense on the tube surfaces in contact with cooler earth temperatures. Provision must be made to drain this condensation away or into the ground. Earth-tube condensation can be used to reduce humidity. The growth of mold can be a problem in the tube.

Ventilation and Cooling

Every climate offers a number of moder-ate-temperature hours per year between 55° to 75°F (12.8° to 23.9°C) when outdoor air can be directly used for indoor ventilation, cooling and comfort. Not only can operable windows and strategically located and operable vents be provided for inductive ventilation, but the main-entry door and other full-size door openings can be securely used for greater amounts of intake air. A practical and cost-effective method for such ventilation that can directly control wind motion as well as inductive ventilation consists of an outer, screened, fully louvered, weather-stripped door; an inner, well-insulated, magnetic or foam weather-stripped metal or wood door; and a threshold that provides a tight air seal. The outer door should be deadlocked with a turn-release bolt, as should the inner door (with like keys for convenience). The outer, louvered door can act as a full-scale ventilator in mild and warm weather with the inner door (provided with a weighted doorstop for incremental positions) acting as a full-scale air-control damper. In cold weather, the outer louvered door can be readily made into a storm door by applying an insulative panel with a relief valve or an insulative thermal blanket with an iron-rod magnetic release at the bottom. These weather elements can be attached by means of a complete Velcro peripheral band (except for vacuum air relief at the bottom that would allow the door to be opened). Be sure to offset the door knobs and allow a depth factor for them.

Sunspaces can in particular enjoy the benefit of this full-scale, louvered-door arrangement. Screened, metal louvers can be more efficiently used for intensive ventilation and cooling. Cross ventilation, stack action, and negative-pressure wind ventilation can also be beneficially employed.

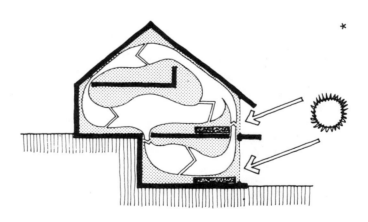

building acting as a natural convection solar-heat pump

A more difficult but important question is how to provide effective roof-ridge or high-position exhaust of interior air. Clerestory windows that open (whether to the north, east, south, or west) are not the answer. Either the indoor environment has be be pressurized by outside wind that enters by inductive ventilation (that works by interior stack action and may be aided by solar-heated roof plenums, wind turbines, or air-inductive exhaust stacks) or the form of the architecture itself can create negative-pressure exhaust caused by external wind movement over the form.

In humid climates with warm and hot periods, ceiling fans can move interior air for more effective physical-body cooling. It is well to use adjustable-speed fans to match perceptions of personal comfort. The Florida Solar Energy Center has prepared information on natural cooling in humid regions (see references).

Housing for the Elderly

As our population ages, our national housing needs are changing. The question is how to preserve human independence, as well as opportunity, for our aging citizens. By the year 2020, Americans over 60 years of age will comprise 25 percent of our total adult population. Now and in the near future this represents a formidable reservoir of human potential, as well as a mounting need.

New California State regulations have addressed this growing population need through the concept of "granny housing." The aging female population exceeds its male counterpart, hence the designation "granny," but not to be forgotten are the surviving men nor the couples who age together. Basically, the premise is that add-on housing units not over 600 square feet of a fully sustainable nature with kitchen and bath can serve this purpose.

The basic guidelines from the California "secondary dwelling units" regulations are summarized as follows:

> The add-on units are allowed only in single-family residential zones on lots where there is only one existing residence; a minimum lot size restriction is specified. The new unit must comply with all current housing and building codes.
> The secondary unit must have a separate entrance. It must be attached by common wall(s), floor, or ceiling; breeze-ways are not permitted. An existing garage or carport cannot be converted. One covered or uncovered parking space is required for the add-on unit, plus parking for the existing dwelling must be provided. The occupancy can be no more than two persons.

While this concept flies in the face of conventional zoning and neighborhood protection, it does promise both a security and extendability of vital living values to the elderly. The question is how to preserve the integrity of existing neighborhoods while giving hope and concern to a large segment of need in our society.

City, county, and state planning and zoning need such land-use accommodation. Care and wisdom are needed in legislation and administration along with the assistance of the architecture profession. Not only should such housing developments be encouraged, but they should be accomplished with maximum protection of the surrounding neighborhood. The automobile is a problem for access and space use that must be addressed in such increases of housing density.

Although "granny housing" may be built to fulfill an urgent and expanding need, the occupancy by other than older persons is most probable. How to handle such occurrence without the intrusions of increased noise and other disturbances is imperative for the peace and composure of the neighborhood. Density itself does not necessarily have to have a negative implication. More self-enforcing regulation with the neighborhood itself empowered to sustain monitoring and control, as well as closer expert scrutiny of all add-on buildings before a building permit is issued are essential for neighborhood quality.

Increased density astutely planned can add to neighborhood security. More people (as it were) in somewhat closer proximity can monitor and protect the interests of the total community. It is important to develop collective feelings and concern for mutual well-being and physical protection.

The majority of the plans and designs in this book are ideal for "granny," add-on, free standing, or multiple attached housing. Senior citizens as well as modest-budget persons and families can be well accommodated by these affordable, passive solar, low-energy-demand homes.

Housing for the Handicapped

All of us are handicapped in one way or another. However, persons in a wheelchair need barrier-free living spaces. General provisions needed include 36-inch (91.4 centimeter) wide doors, door hardware and light switches located at a lower level, wardrobe-closet doors that slide or are eliminated, raised electrical outlets, and altered kitchen cabinets. Undercounter leg room is always needed for a wheelchair, and bathrooms need handrails as well as appropriately sized and configured tub and shower facilities.

Every serious human handicap has its own range of physical limitation. The architect, designer, and the handicapped person need to coordinate their efforts toward adequate design resolutions. Ramps may have to replace stairs and special devices or equipment may be necessary for mobility, convenience, and activities of the disabled or handicapped person.

Drafting Procedures

Several simplistic, residential, plan-drafting procedures can reduce time and construction; notably, by using a 4-foot (1.2 meter), numbered, architectural-scaled grid system almost all dimensions can be eliminated, except for those that are individually critical. Furthermore, in the field the general contractor and/or all subcontractors can benefit by reduced initial layout time and ease of reference in communication. Another time-saving procedure is to simplify all door, window, and other details by avoiding design that calls for special solutions. Another is to use short-form specifications and to review the project carefully with the contractor so he will understand the intent of the drawings more clearly. Computer drafting will undoubtedly become a more common practice. Organization in drafting procedures that can lead to computer resolutions will aid the transition from manual methods.

Plan from the interior out by blocking in all furniture and equipment on the preliminary schematics. Use transparency prints for furniture, equipment, electrical, mechanical, and active and passive energy systems layouts.

Summary

To sum up this chapter on design and architecture, the following list of critical factors for total, integrative energy design should form a fundamental reference for the design process.

- All elements of the site, architecture, interior, and people that interface with the microclimate and the earth are part of the holistic-energy system.
- Topographic landscaping should be designed to reduce climatic extremes.
- All hours of the day and seasons of the year should be considered as to time-period space use and variant occupant needs.
- Design solutions should be appropriate for each specific project.
- An economic priority should be established regarding the use of construction methods, materials, labor, and energy-demand use.
- Passive energy systems and energy conservation should take precedence over active and mechanical energy systems.
- Proper control and controls over both natural and applied energies should prevail.
- Trade-offs in costs and benefits should be calculated on a life-cycle basis.
- Human health, vitality, and psychologic well-being should be a top priority in regard to indoor environmental control.
- Total, integrative energy design is complex but most economically and functionally rewarding. Engage an architect and/or designer with energy knowledge and experience.

Chapter 4

Materials and Components for Affordable Homes

Economic Factors

The choice of materials plays an important economic role in construction. The particular use, placement, and total direct and indirect costs of materials affect the cost of the completed home. Long-term factors of energy demand, ease of maintenance, and durability are critical to economic issues. All options should be judiciously exercised in the quest for the most affordable home.

Not only are the initial costs of materials important, but also the skill and amount of labor needed to incorporate them into the construction. Direct labor costs include cutting, forming, and securing materials in place, together with the cost of the material itself. Indirect labor costs result from preparation work, such as excavation, scaffolding, temporary power, shoring, and layout — plus the effects these costs have upon mechanical and electrical work. The ratio of labor-to-materials cost should always be kept in mind.

Each choice of materials and method of construction should be evaluated regarding their holistic-energy significance within the completed project. In all cases, energy-demand factors relate directly to economics. A reasonable procedure is to cost-factor all construction materials and subcontract needs. Then evaluate the categorized cost increments. Define the most cost-effective priorities with the least compromise — or none at all — with optimal energy conservation and practicality. Good planning and design can hold total construction, life-cycle, energy, and maintenance costs to a minimum.

A primary planning and design question is whether to use on-site and local construction materials, regenerative materials, recycled materials, or to take advantage of partial or completely manufactured components. These options relate in part to financing methods and the number of units being constructed.

Part of the cost of construction materials involves their manufacture, transportation to the site, and assembly. All of these processes consume considerable amounts of energy; in fact, more energy is used in constructing a building than in many years of operation.[28] Using locally produced, regenerative or on-site materials can help to reduce the energy cost of construction. The use of energy-intensive materials such as aluminum, steel, glass, and plastics should be minimized where possible.

Basic Building Materials

The following paragraphs describe the energy and construction factors of common materials used for home building.

Wood. Most homes and light commercial buildings are constructed of wood, a regenerative product. Wood is the material most workable with ordinary tools. Its particular usefulness is its ability to be sawn, shaped, nailed, bored, tenoned, glued, painted, or stained. Different types of wood have different workability, structural (tensile and compressive strength, hardness), and finishing characteristics. Wood is the most economical and adaptable building material from rough framing to fine cabinetwork. Its principal drawback is that it supports combustion and infestations of insects and fungi. However, wood can be made chemically resistant to fire and infestation for foundations and retaining walls or portions exposed to water, moisture, and the earth.

Wood is readily available in practical, precut dimensions. However, care must be taken in choosing the correct grade, type, and quality for each specific application.

_____
[28]Mazria, p. 115.

For example, for siding, wood strength is less important than good weathering properties or good receptivity of paint or other finishes. Another point is that the way a board is sawn affects its strength and durability. Also, air- or kiln-dried lumber has greater nail-holding power than green or partially seasoned lumber and also holds paint and preservatives better. (See Ken Kern's book, *The Owner-Built Home,* for more information about wood and wood construction[29]).

Glass. Glass is the most widely used glazing material. Float glass is the type most commonly used in home construction when clear, flat glass is desired. In this process, molten glass is floated on a surface of molten metal, slowly cooled (annealed), and then cut to the desired size.

Glass can be transparent, translucent, or opaque. It can be patterned, tinted, or reflective. In solar energy applications where high solar-radiation transmission is desired, low-iron or water-white glass is often used, since iron oxide in glass causes absorption losses in the visible and infrared spectral regions (which can be seen by the green color present when looking at the edge of a sheet of glass). Of course, "solar glass" is more expensive than regular float glass.

Glass has many advantages: excellent transmissivity and optical clarity; high resistance to ultraviolet radiation, weathering, chemical deterioration, and abrasions; low thermal expansion and contraction; long service life and high service temperature; ease of maintenance; and very low infrared (heat) transmission. Glass has several well-known drawbacks also: heavy weight; low impact resistance; relatively high cost; dif-

ficulty in site fabrication; and it requires a relatively large amount of energy to manufacture (11,438 Btus/lb. [8.29 cal/gram]).[30]

Glass can be strengthened by tempering, which involves reheating the glass followed by rapid cooling. Tempered glass is four to five times stronger than regular annealed glass. When broken, tempered glass disintegrates into small, blunt particles instead of sharp shards. Tempering will increase distortion of reflected images in all types of glass, and tempered glass cannot be cut at the job site and must be ordered cut to size. Tempered glass is required for physical safety in all glass of exterior walls installed within 18 inches (45.7 centimeters) of the floor.

Glass block is another glazing option available in either single-cavity, double-cavity, or solid form with a variety of surface treatments and patterns. Single- and double-cavity glass block is made by fusing together two molded halves at high temperatures. After cooling, the trapped air inside becomes very dry, preventing condensation and producing good insulating properties. Transmission can range from 5 percent for reflective block to about 80 percent for clear block.

Glass blocks can increase privacy; provide greater resistance to vandalism, forced entry, and fire; reduce sound transmission; increase ambient light levels; and control solar heat gain, light transmision, and light direction. A drawback is the elimination or distortion of view with most types of glass block, and the installed cost of the block.

Concrete. Concrete is versatile and can be shaped to almost any form. It has a large thermal mass and high compressive (loading) strength. And when reinforced with

steel, its tensile strength (ability to resist lengthwise stress) can be increased also, reducing the necessary thickness. Concrete should be selectively specified and reinforced to meet structural needs. It can be poured in place, laid as a flat slab, applied as a sprayed-in-place mixture, be precast and prestressed, or be mixed with earth, sawdust, glass fibers, or other materials. Unconventional composite mixtures should be strength-tested prior to construction.

Concrete can be premixed or mixed on site. Premixed concrete is somewhat more economical for larger cubic-yard needs. Framing, pouring, placing, and finishing costs can be lowered by a home owner's own labor. Usually concrete block walls (more energy-intensive in manufacture) can be installed at less cost. In any case, surface waterproofing should be adequate to prevent intrusion of subsurface water or moisture.

The major disadvantage of concrete is its susceptibility to shrinkage cracking.[31] This tendency can be lessened by using a minimum amount of water in concrete mixing; allowing the concrete to mix for several minutes after it is uniform in appearance; and making sure of thorough settlement and compaction. All of these measures increase the compressive strength of the concrete so that the proportions of cement can be reduced, thereby reducing shrinkage cracking.[32] Newly poured concrete should always be protected against freezing. Concrete firmly sets in 14 days and reaches its full hardness in 21 days. Be certain that your concrete contains no radioactivity within its materials.

Brick. Brick has a large thermal mass useful in passive solar systems for energy

---

[29]Ken Kern, *The Owner-Built Home* (New York: Charles Scribner's Sons, 1975).

[30]Mazria, p. 117.

[31]Kern, p. 195.

[32]Ibid, pp. 195-196.

storage. Brick is durable but is energy intensive in manufacture. It also requires experience in laying. Workmanship is important, especially in regard to the bond between the brick and the mortar, which is critical to the strength of the wall and its resistance to rain penetration.[33]

Brick with a magnesium additive has a higher thermal conductivity (about six times greater) than that of common brick. Higher conductivity will result in smaller air temperature fluctuations in a space using bricks for heat storage because of more rapid heat transfer from the surface of the material to its interior, where the heat is stored for use in the evening.[34] Be certain that the brick you use has no radioactive properties.

Tile. Ceramic or concrete tile is a very durable but more expensive material. It is available in a wide range of sizes, colors, and surface finishes. Tile used for solar applications, such as covering a concrete slab floor, should be a medium to dark color and have an unglazed or a mat-glazed finish, not glossy.

Drywall. Drywall (gypsum board, sheet rock, plaster board) offers fire resistance, relatively low cost, and an economical surface to paint. Skill is required to finish the joints (spackling), and drywall is heavy and cumbersome to handle. Standard, ½-inch (12.7 millimeter) drywall has an R-value of 0.45.[35] Some codes may require ⅝-inch (16 millimeter) fire-rated material in certain locations, such as in stairways.[36] Conventional ½-inch (12.7 millimeter) drywall with

joints has a fire rating of 20 minutes; ⅝-inch (16 millimeter) drywall is fire rated for one hour.

Plywood and Particle Board. These materials are commonly used in almost all home construction and are usually prevalent in larger amounts in mobile homes. Particle board and interior-grade plywood contain urea formaldehyde resin as a bonding agent; exterior-grade plywood contains phenol formaldehyde.[37] These products emit formaldehyde gas, which causes respiratory and other health problems in humans. Urea formaldehyde outgasses ten times more emissions than phenol formaldehyde.[38] All exposed plywood and particle board, along with furniture and cabinets made of plywood and particle board, should be sealed against outgassing. Latex paint will work; for more serious problems a formaldehyde vapor-barrier sealant known as Hyde-check is available from the Mortell Company (550 North Hobbie Avenue, Kankakee, Illinois, 60901), or it might be found in some mobile home supply stores.[39] (More information about indoor pollution is to be found in Chapter 6.)

Plastic Laminates. Plastic laminates, such as Formica, are expensive and energy-intensive to manufacture. They require skill in installation. These materials are easy to clean and durable and come in a variety of colors. Smooth surfaces are required for lamination because distinct wood grains can telegraph through the laminate.

Insulation. Insulation comes in many different forms and configurations. The basic, generic types are rolls, batts, blankets, loose

fill, rigid beam, reflective foil or paper, sprayed in place, or foamed in place. Each type should be tailored to specific applications best suited for that form. Each type has unique advantages and disadvantages. In all cases, urea formaldehyde foam should not be used. This type of foamed-in-place insulation had been banned by the Consumer Product Safety Commission as a health hazard because of formaldehyde outgassing caused by improper mixing and installation. (The ban was allowed to expire in 1983).

Factors to consider when selecting insulation include: R-value, fire resistance, water and moisture resistance, maximum service temperature, density, ease of installation, effectiveness as a vapor barrier, and cost. For more information on insulation and correct installation techniques, see the November-December 1982 issue of *New Shelter* magazine.[40]

Cured polystyrene board is the necessary base for acrylic-based stucco-like exterior coatings thinly applied over nylon reinforcement mesh (such as Sto, Settef, Dryvit). A distinct thermal advantage of these materials is effective encasement of the architectural envelope, lessening infiltration and preventing thermal bridging of the framing, masonry, or concrete structure.

Roofing

The selection of roofing materials, their application, details of use, and their color and durability are always problematic. So-

---

[33]Ibid, p. 181.

[34]Mazria, p. 141.

[35]Ibid., p. 352.

[36]Eugene Eccli, ed., *Low-Cost Energy-Efficient Shelter for the Owner and Builder* (Emmaus, Pa.: Rodale Press, 1976), p. 117.

[37]Lafavore, pp. 21, 22.

[38]Ibid.

[39]Ibid.

[40]Frederic S. Langa, "Enough Is Enough"; Bob Flower, "So You Need More?"; Tom Wilson, "How *Not* to Install Insulation"; and, Bob Flower, "Buying the Right Kind," *New Shelter,* vol. 3, no. 9, Nov.-Dec. 1982, pp. 20-24, 25-28, and 29-33, resp.

called "flat" roofs should have a pitch of at least ¼ inch to the foot for adequate drainage. Asphalt, wood shingles, concrete tile, or metal roofs (depending on the severity of the winter climate) should be at a 3-to-12-foot pitch for moderate climates and a 4-to-12-foot pitch or more for more severe climates. A local roofing contractor should be consulted on roof pitch, materials, and costs.

Fiberglass asphaltic shingles are less expensive than wood shingles, tile, or seamed metal. The color should be in accordance with the climatic color chart (see Appendix). White marble chips on built-up roofs will reflect summer sun back to the sky, reducing interior temperatures. A more reflective roof is one manufactured with an aluminum surface that reflects over 80 percent of the sun's radiation. This is particularly effective for roof surfaces directly in front of solar collectors or clerestory windows. In all cases, special attention should be paid to roof flashing to ensure watertight seals and no leakage.

Building Components

The following paragraphs describe major components in home construction and give recommendations concerning energy and economic factors.

Doors. All exterior doors should be insulated, weather-stripped, and have thresholds that avoid air infiltration. Less expensive hollow-core doors of Masonite or paint-grade plywood can be used for interior openings. A louvered, wooden, outer entrance door can serve as a screen door in summer. Sunscreened fabric (with many tiny, metal, horizontal louvers) backed with metal bars and deadlocked can also be a

sliding or
hinged panels
can cover glass
areas at night

provision for a security door in summer that allows for ventilation. Addition of an insulative panel or blanket secured with Velcro and a magnetic air release at the bottom will provide cold-weather storm protection for either type of ventilation door.

In some of the plans in this book, sunspaces and other openings are fitted with side-sliding, double-glazed patio doors. These doors should be designed in wood, metal, or vinyl frames to avoid thermal bridging and have foot locks for secure ventilation. These and all windows should have insect screening. Interior sliding glass doors can be a less expensive type, with wooden or metal frames, single-pane tempered glass, and no provisions to prevent thermal bridging.

Windows. Windows can be used for daylight, view, ventilation, and passive solar heating and cooling. Using fixed windows for light and view and insulated, strategically located operable vents for ventilation and cooling can be more energy-effective but be greater in cost.

Operable windows should be selectively glazed (single-, double-, or triple-pane as needed), tight-fitting, and have thermal-break frames. Vinyl-covered window members prevent deterioration. Awning-type or casement windows are preferred to side-sliding or double-hung windows because of better ventilation properties. Check local building codes to be certain windows meet lighting, ventilating, and exiting requirements (especially in bedrooms).

Movable Insulation. Movable insulation is very effective in reducing energy losses in cold climates since glazing has a heat loss many times greater than well-insulated exterior wall sections. To function properly, movable insulation must meet certain criteria:

- It should have adequate insulative value and fit tightly over window or skylight openings.
- It should be easily movable.
- Occupants or mechanical controls must operate the movable insulation at the appropriate times.
- Adequate stacking or storing space must be provided to prevent interference with full, passive solar gains. (Stacking or storing space should always be provided for in the original design.)

Movable insulation comes in many different forms; namely, rolling, hinged, sliding, or removable insulative blinds; thermal draperies or shades; and shutters. Also available are insulating miniblinds that use a plastic honeycomb structure with heat-reflective films to achieve a high R-value.

Ordinary draperies are a poor choice, because they do not fit tightly to the window opening and the space between the glazing and drape acts as a convective heat channel. (This heat loss can be reduced by placing a valance above the drape, but local convective air flow will still be present near the glazing.)

Large south-facing glass areas in passive solar designs, skylights, sloped glazing, and northside windows present the greatest cold-weather heat loss from the interior. Movable insulation is particularly important to such architectural openings. Northside windows should remain covered at all times during cold weather, except when an occupant wishes to see outdoors or use north daylighting.

Almost all movable insulative window coverings can benefit by using infrared-reflective materials to return the long-wavelength heat energy of the interior back to the room space. The most effective movable insulation, from a thermal-advantage standpoint, is various forms applied to the exterior of a glazed opening, often operable from the interior. These installations also provide a greater amount of physical security.

Movable insulation has several drawbacks. For one, most types are nearly or completely opaque to sunlight, so beneficial daylight can be obscured. Furthermore, most movable insulative window coverings do not provide a selective control over uniform distribution, direction, or the amount of desired daylighting or exterior view. Some forms of movable insulation can impede fire safety. The necessity and inconvenience of time-of-day operation that movable insula-

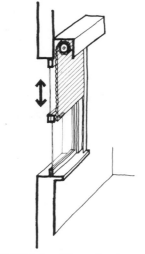

insulated rolling shade

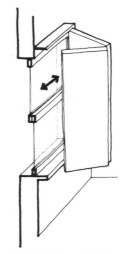

insulated folding shutter

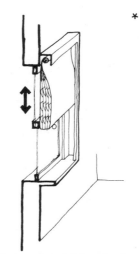

reflective expandable shade

tion imposes upon dwelling occupants is a major constraint to its use. For these and cost and performance reasons, alternatives to movable insulation should be considered.

Avoiding sloped glazing for atriums, sunspaces, attached greenhouses, or other portions of the architecture is one way to reduce the need for movable insulation and eliminate serious energy loss to the night sky and by convective windchill. Sunspaces without movable insulation, not continously occupied, can be effective thermal buffers through both heating and cooling seasons. Using indirect or isolated passive or hybrid solar systems thermally buffered from the interior can minimize direct glazed areas and still provide solar heating (by convective-air induction or powered fans and blowers). Several home designs presented use these concepts. Daylight can be controlled by these methods.

One architectural strategy that increases daylighting and decreases the need for movable insulation is the slot clerestory combined with a reflective roof and overhead canopy reflector. Direct solar radiation is concentrated through a relatively narrow, horizontal band of glass that, along with the contributory reflection, will optimize winter daylighting and thermal gains. The benefit of the slot window is that it "sees" less of the clear sky than a conventional clerestory skylight, thus experiencing less interior energy loss. If correctly designed, the overhead canopy will shade the clerestory slot near the equinox and through the summer season, providing soft, reflective daylighting while the roof reflects most of the direct sun back to the sky.

Other architectural design methods can be used to reduce customary passive solar

glazed areas without sacrificing thermal performance or effective daylighting. Exterior white marble chips or concrete, brick, or stone pavers painted white can be used to increase solar radiation reflection into the interior. Sunspaces, including the flooring material, can be reflective white or very light colors to increase secondary gains through glazing between the sunspaces and the interior.

Architectural design, along with thermal-responsive glazing and various systems for intercepting solar radiation, can reduce or reasonably eliminate the use of movable window and skylight coverings. When movable insulation is used, cost comparisons among various types should be made, and the expense of the insulation should be included as an element of the total architectural and project budget.

Storage of Materials and Components

During construction, building materials and interior finishing components should be protected against weather, loss, and physical damage. Valuable materials should be stored in a protected area under lock and key.

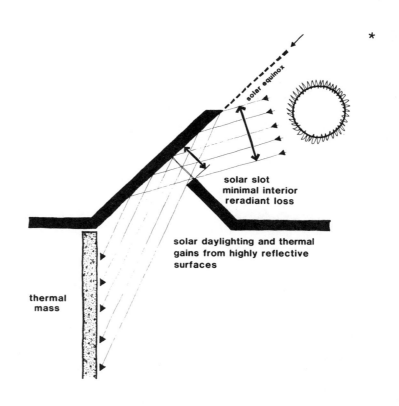

solar equinox

*

solar slot
minimal interior
reradiant loss

solar daylighting and thermal
gains from highly reflective
surfaces

thermal
mass

On-Site Materials

In many nonindustrial areas of the world and during our own pioneer era in the United States, on-site materials have been the only materials available for constructing a home. Stone, trees, earth, vegetation, and sometimes, animal products, have been used to form unique, indigenous housing.

"Modern" construction materials and methods tend to ignore the possibilities of using on-site materials, even though these substances often possess climatic and energy advantages. On-site earth, however, is still occasionally used in some areas of the United States as a building material. Earth technologies are not necessarily "dirt cheap." They are usually labor intensive and sometimes require heavy equipment. However, if low-cost labor is available or individuals are willing to invest their own sweat labor, earth technologies can be economically attractive.

Basically, these technologies are defined as:

Rammed Earth. Moistened earth is rammed in sequential layers within a wood or metal form.

Adobe. Earth of an appropriate consistency is placed into block forms, often with straw or other reinforcement and then is sun-baked upon removal from the form.

Stabilized Earth. Substances that form a gel can be injected into the earth to stabilize the soil.

Soils Concrete. For concrete flat work, small amounts of cement are added to earth and then watered with a hose to form concrete.

Matrix Earth Construction. Massive amounts of earth can be packed between interior or exterior walls to densify the thermal mass.

Structural Consolidated Earth. Various waste materials that could include paper, sawdust, or other fibrous materials, and other bitumens with sulfonic acid or small quantities of cement can be used to achieve structural, thermal, or insulative walls. Preconstruction strength tests should be made when using unconventional material combinations.

Earth Berming. Berms can be strategically formed around architecture to reduce climatic impacts.

Earth-Sheltering. Earth-sheltering includes completely underground to partially earth-sheltered buildings.

Cut-and-Fill. Almost all construction uses cut-and-fill; however, this technique can be used for extensive architectural land forming.

Using Waste or Salvageable Materials

Waste and salvage materials remain a largely untapped productive resource. Almost all waste materials can be recycled into a productive purpose. A primary economic question is, does the preparation, processing, and use of waste materials exceed in effort and energy the use of new materials? A secondary question is, does the cost of waste disposal or correcting its environmental harm cause further economic burdens? The comparative transportation costs between new and waste materials should not be neglected as an economic factor, nor should the technologic costs for their incorporation as construction elements.

The vast range of waste materials is a storehouse of opportunity. Waste materials are sometimes adaptable in their indigenous forms while others need to be processed or combined with other materials. Almost every waste material can be practically used in construction. Waste products of glass, metal, concrete, brick, stone, asphalt, tile, marble, ceramics, chemicals, fluids, and oil can be adapted to architecture. The size, form, color, and other physical properties of natural or manufactured waste products, substances, and materials make up their individual forms. They can become elements of architectural enclosure, reinforcement, structure, texture, and finish.

The most common problem in using waste materials is lack of technical information about their performance, compatibility, durability, and unqualified applications cost. A more thorough evaluation of the amount of waste available and guidelines for its use are needed.

Other more transient or amorphous waste materials, such as organic fluids, gases, and solids, can also be recycled. More imagination and technical ability is generally needed to use these less stable forms of matter. All of the fluid and solid wastes from bathrooms can be reclaimed for the fertilization of growing plants and their thermal aspects can be used for supplemental energy.

United States citizens are the most wasteful people in the world; thus, we have the greatest opportunity to use this resource constructively. As inflation and high material and labor costs impact the economics of architectural construction, it is likely that more people will become aware of the construction potential that exists in waste.

Chapter 5

Construction

The choice of construction method has an impact similar to materials choices in terms of maintenance, durability, energy demand, initial and ongoing costs, and other economic factors that accompany a complete home. All the various options are interrelated in the quest for the most affordable home. Construction methods vary in practicality and cost from location to location. As with materials, each construction method should be weighed as to its total, integrative, energy design significance to the entire project.

Construction Procedures

There are many ways to go about constructing a home, ranging from a general contractor to an owner's own labor. The various procedures and options are discussed below.

General Contractor. A general contractor can simply and quickly build a model home based on most of the conceptual plans and designs in this book. With good planning and logistics, most of these plans of less than 1,000 square feet (92.9 square meters) could be constructed in four to six weeks, with larger homes somewhat longer.

Because up-front construction financing, land-investment holding, and marketing time can be minimal, the sales price and contractor's time-factor profits can result in a bottom-line home cost. The packaging of a number of housing units should be attractive to financing people because of the probabilities of rapid money turnover and the security of more living units for the amount of invested capital.

Since passive solar, other natural energy systems, and conservation design are integral elements of the architecture and only a small amount of supplemental heating (such as electric hydronic baseboard) might be needed in cold weather, the proportionate utility costs should be very small. Thus, utility costs should not be competitive with the home owner's ability to make mortgage payments.

Speculative Developer. Most developers want to leverage their projects; i.e., use small sums of money to get the greatest capital return. Most of the designs presented lend themselves to fast market response with little initial capital investment, although profit per unit may be small. The time-period volume of units compensates for and might exceed other forms of invest-

ment return. Sellers of land are likely to be more interested in partial releases of land for a project that offers construction activity and continuity.

Modular Home Builders. All of the plans are developed on a 4-foot (1.2 meter) module for economy in materials use and ease in construction. Most are suitable for modular building. Wood foundations with appropriately treated lumber can effectively reduce costs and construction time.

Some modular builders offer a customized service. The potential home owner can present a conceptual plan such as those in this book and the modular company will estimate and fabricate to the potential owner's needs.

Subcontract Construction. In many areas of the United States, subcontractors offer poured-in-place foundations, construction framing, building-envelope enclosure, roofing, finish carpentry, cabinetwork, or glazing, as well as electrical and mechanical work. By "subbing out" all of this work, the potential home owner can relieve himself or herself of trying to develop his/her own home building skills. However, the more that the potential owner can learn or know about construction and its vast array of pitfalls, the better off he/she will be. Most individuals can provide some unskilled work and also do the painting.

Owner-built. A knowledgeable and skilled potential owner can take on as much of the construction work as his or her own abilities will allow. Some of the presented home designs would be suitable for owner building. It is important for the potential home owner not to be overconfident but be adequately enthusiastic and patient with the building process. As stated above, many pitfalls and risks can accompany building a home that must be met by adequate knowledge and organization.

Participatory Labor and Pooled Financing. One procedure for owner-built construction is to develop a cooperative labor and, possibly, financial pool. Two or more individuals can pool their money to buy the needed materials and help each other with their own skills and sweat labor to build a home. In turn, after the home acquires its permanent mortgage financing, the monetary and labor effort can then be used to produce subsequent homes. This procedure in no way excludes the use of necessary subcontract work.

One shortcoming of this cooperative means of building (and, possibly, financing) the project is that the individuals involved can fall into disagreement, become disillusioned with construction, or feel they are getting the short end of the bargain.

Some Cautions to Observe. The potential owner should be certain that the gathering of construction estimates is complete before undertaking the construction. Financing money should be adequate and be available incrementally as needed.

Contractors or subcontractors should be checked on the projects they have built and their general reputations. Be certain contractors and subcontractors carry worker's compensation and liability insurance. As a home owner, you should take out contingent-liability insurance or check on insurance requirements that will be needed if you are your own builder.

Designs and plans have to be approved under the applicable jurisdictional codes and regulations in your area. An architect or home designer knowledgeable about passive and active solar design should be hired to prepare the final construction plans. A qualified engineer should be hired for soils testing and foundation and structural design evaluation.

Developing and Building

The conceptual plans and designs in this book are ideal for speculative building for several reasons: a low relative cost per unit; possibilities for intensive land use; attached housing capability; expeditious capital development; and, good market turnover potential.

Astute, integrative planning, care for solar access, and responsive architecture should add up to privacy, quietness, and landscaping that dominates the architecture. Protective landscaping regulations are more essential for compact homes with small sites than for larger homes on bigger sites. The smaller the average living unit is, the more the potential buyer will consider aspects of the total neighborhood community.

Compact passive solar communities need greater than average natural-energy-conscious land planners, architects, or designers. The developer, contractor, and financing agency are key elements of the develop-ment team that likewise should have a vision of the compact solar community as a self-sustaining, delightful human environment. Marketing should consider not only initial cost, but also long-term economic savings.

General Construction Methods

This section describes the major methods used in home construction.

Frame. Wood frame is the most common method of residential construction. Dimensional lumber and plywood is used for framing, decking, and sheathing.

Masonry. Masonry construction includes brick, concrete block, or stone. It is more labor intensive than frame but can provide an effective thermal mass.

Concrete. Concrete construction includes sprayed-on or poured-in-place concrete for walls, floors, and roofs. It provides a good thermal mass but requires the cost of forming and strengthening with reinforcement.

Earth-Shelter, Earth-Coupling, and Underground. Underground construction, earth-coupling, earth-sheltering, and climate-control earth berms are all options that should be explored. Principal concerns should be daylighting, waterproofing problems, ventilation, radon-gas pollution, and the possibility of higher construction costs. Earth-sheltering and underground construction can enhance security and protection from heavy winds, tornadoes, and atomic fallout. Beware of areas where flooding can occur or with high water tables.

Earth Technology. Earth construction can be with adobe, rammed earth, soils solidification, earth concrete, and other admixtures. It is generally labor intensive.

Metal. Metal construction of steel, aluminum, or other metals is thermally conductive and, thus, requires careful insulation. Its most appropriate use is for passive design, where conductive surfaces are desirable.

Economics in Construction

Saving money in construction starts literally from the ground up. Careful use of on-site earth for berms, earth-sheltering, and fill that avoids any subsequent earth moving is advised. Saving good topsoil for reuse is another economic measure. The more that standard-form sections can be used, foundation steps or cutouts eliminated, and breaks in the foundation wall avoided, the more money will be saved. Similarly, the more that framing is used to its full length with net waste for roof, wall, and floor members, the more cost figures will be improved. The plans have been designed to avoid waste when cutting dimensional lumber and sheet materials.

Adequate allowance should always be made for ease in plumbing, electrical wiring, active and passive solar, and mechanical work. The more that these systems are integratively planned for directness, ease of application, and avoidance of conflict, the more total labor costs will be proportionately lower. Avoid costly details of doors, windows, eaves, stairways, baseboards, and casings. Prioritize all of the energy conservation features for special attention as to air infiltration , solar heating, inductive cool-

ing, and insulation for their long-term economic values.

Good materials and labor logistics must apply if fast-track construction is desired. Appliances and equipment acquisition should be lined up right from the start of the project. All wooden stairways or metal or wooden spiral stairs should be prefabricated. Manufactured furniture and cabinetwork should be substituted for built-ins. Bargain hunting for materials, devices, energy-conserving appliances, and equipment is a good strategy, but be cautious of cheap quality items and materials.

Construction Specifics

This section describes and gives recommendations for various building procedures and conservation measures needed to achieve high quality, tight construction.

Excavation and Earth Handling. Earth is a valuable construction resource. Its thermal mass, atmospheric buffering, and insulative properties can be used for an effective construction material, as a temperature- and water-controlling embankment, and as berms. The soil of each site has its specific properties. The surface soil (topsoil) should be evaluated for its fertility. The subsoils should be evaluated for their compressive strength, compaction, porosity, expansiveness, lateral pressure, moisture, level of water table, and inherent composition for use as a building material. Useful topsoil should be diligently saved and used for gardens and landscaping.

Cut-and-fill should be predetermined to minimize earth handling; however, backfilling and compaction around the building structure should not occur until the foundation and flooring systems are structurally

in place. Foundations, exterior insulation, and subsurface drainage systems should be installed prior to backfilling. Compaction should be adequate to avoid sinking of the backfill.

Footings and Foundations. The most common footing and foundation used for residential construction is poured concrete. Reinforcement should be engineered to meet soils tests requirements. Soil conditions, the amount of groundwater, and the depth of the frost line all influence the choice of materials and the design of foundations.[41]

One way to reduce both material and labor costs and expedite foundation work is by constructing an all-wood foundation. Special pressure-treated lumber (made acceptable to building code requirements) is used for wood foundations. Manufacturers recommendations should be followed absolutely!

Concrete Slab on Grade. Concrete slab-on-grade floors can be effectively used for cold and warm climates. The advantage is a floor with thermal mass. Other advantages are elimination of necessary ventilation and insulation, insect infestations, and dampness that often accompany underfloor crawl space.

In cold climates, footings and foundation walls should (and are usually required by code to) extend below the subsurface, winter frost line. Insulation (usually blue Styrofoam) should be applied to the outer surface of the foundation wall and extend from above grade to the footing. In climates with extended cold winters, insulation should also be placed under the slab floor around its perimeter. In very cold climates, extend the insulation completely under the concrete slab floor. A way to increase the

---

[41]Kern, pp. 270, 271.

thermal mass of the floor for passive solar collection is to thicken it to 6 inches (15 centimeters) in the direct solar radiation path. Or, insulation could be placed at the footing line, covered with a layer of earth for added mass, and then topped with the concrete slab. Take care to insulate at the perimeter edge of the slab to prevent thermal losses.

Tight Construction. Tight construction requires good workmanship and attention to details. Framing doesn't have to be perfect, but square-cut members, tight-fitting blocking, and level and plumb work can reduce air infiltration and exfiltration. Air leakage in particular occurs at the sill plate line that rests upon the foundation wall. Compressible insulation should be installed under and on the outside of the plate, and caulking should be placed on the outside joint. Another trouble spot is the band joist, usually a board placed on its edge above the horizontal sill plate and also found between stories of a house. This should also be sealed and insulated.

Other voids that allow air infiltration can be found around window and door frames and electrical boxes. Around window and door casings, a foam sealant should be used; around the outlet boxes, it should be a noncombustible material. Exterior siding, sheeting, or other materials should have tight joints. A continuous vapor barrier of 6-mil (152 micrometer) polyethylene should be installed under all interior drywall on the "warm" side of the room. The vapor barrier must be *continuous* through the outer walls and common ceiling and roof rafters, and should be placed on the interior warm side of all insulation.

To ensure tight construction, care must be taken when setting forms and pouring

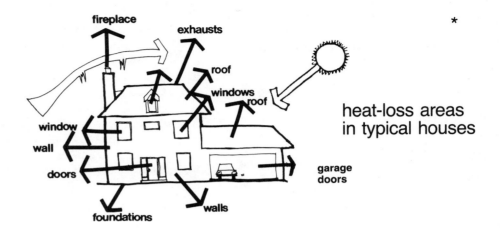

heat-loss areas
in typical houses

concrete foundation walls. Flues and vents need to be accurately fitted, caulked in, and dampered as necessary against unwanted energy loss.

Insulation. Insulation types and thickness should be tailored to your climate. (See recommended insulation levels — Appendix B.) Check the benefits and costs of superinsulation applied as or under the sheathing. Check to see if you can get nailable insulation board.

Inasmuch as the author has chosen to avoid roof trusses for ventilated and sometimes useless attics, it is advised that all roof rafters be well insulated to make lofts, attics, and upper-level spaces more habitable and useful. In humid climates, particular care must be exercised to ventilate eaves or roof members. A "cold roof," designed to prevent edges from icing up with sometimes disastrous results, should be provided for very cold climate areas.

Both partial- and full-foundation walls

should be insulated on the outside with appropriate, rigid, moisture-resistant insulation. In cold climates, most foundation insulation should extend down to the footing. It is most important regading the effect of cold earth temperatures on slab-on-grade floors (particularly thickened concrete or masonry for solar-thermal storage) that an adequately insulated thermal break be provided at the outer edge. Perimeter versus complete placement of insulation under the floor should be determined. Appropriate insulative glass or plastic glazing should be selectively used to match the on-site climatic conditions. An intervening high-transmissivity film between clear glass layers will admit solar radiation but reduce internal energy losses. All sash members should have thermal breaks. All outer doors should be well insulated and have magnetic or other very effective weather stripping.

Most of the energy losses of a home (except for glazed areas) are through the roof; thus, continuous insulation plus tight-fitting insulation between roof rafters, common roof and ceiling members, and outer walls will produce a more energy-efficient house. Selectively superinsulating a vulnerable north wall exposed to cold winter winds and using appropriate insulation on east, south, and west outer walls can be judicious.

Outer Wall Coatings. A stucco-like acrylic coating applied over a heavy nylon mesh attached to polystyrene beadboard can be a system used over frame or concrete. Such materials are known as Sto, Settef, or Dryvit. They all perform in a like manner, literally wrapping insulation around the building and acting as a durable, textured weather coat on the exterior. The great advantage of such coating systems is that thermal bridging is virtually eliminated. Particularly with concrete or masonry interiors, the interior thermal mass that tends to stabilize indoor temperatures is protected from the climate.

Roofing. The main concerns about roofing are weather tightness, durability, thermal reflectivity or absorptivity, conductance, resistance to wind, and appearance. The pitch of the roof and climate have much to do with selection of the roofing system.

Roofing materials have not been illustrated for the sketches in this book because of the wide variety and appropriateness to the climate and neighborhood. Pitched roof systems include asphalt shingles, wood shingles, wood shakes, fired-clay tiles, concrete tiles, and metal roofing. Some have minor thermal resistance, but reflectivity and thermal absorption are more important. Light-colored or specular-surface roofs reflect solar radiation back to the sky. Dark colors absorb heat in proportion to their darkness, texture and mat surface. These properties have a material effect on the energy flows of the building. Furthermore, the more that the sun's radiation is converted to heat, the more that external convection along the roof is accelerated. Acrylic-coated roofs can also be provided over small, specialized areas such as window bays, projecting sunspaces, and small canopies. The manufacturer should be consulted, but, usually, such roofs have to be pitched at 45 degrees or more.

Flat roofs include hot pitched tar or asphalt, which are generally used for residential applications because of their lower cost; single-ply membrane systems; a specular-reflective composite roof that is annealed at the seams with heat; and various forms of other hot, wrapped-roof systems and spray applications. Various types of rigid insulation can be applied under the roofing material (particularly for concrete roofs) to insulate the mass from the atmosphere. To achieve a reflective surface, white marble chips can be used for a protective topping rather than gravel. White coatings and shiny, reflective, aluminized coatings can be applied to roofs with or without gravel for reflectivity.

When habitable roof decks are shown, a conventional built-up roof can be applied and cedar, redwood, or treated wood decks with a ¼-inch (6.4 millimeter) separation of the boards can be installed over continuous wood cleats. Nonrusting nails or screws should be used. Other walking decks can be troweled as a compositional material or, if the deck is structurally adequate, flat concrete pavers can become a traffic surface.

A flat or very low-pitched roof can have more leakage problems than one with a greater pitch. However, on a flat roof in cold regions, the accumulated snow layer can act as an insulative interface. The snow can also act as a reflector for heat gain to solar collectors (with adequate provision for keeping the collectors clean). Gutters under collectors should be heavily reinforced to avoid damage from the avalanche effect of melting snow.

Thin Air Films. In calculating heat losses and gains from a building, the thin air film is taken into account. This one-molecule-thick air interface occurs between the outdoor atmosphere and the surface of the building and between the corresponding interior side of the wall surface and indoor air. Very small, textural surfaces tend to preserve the thin air film. The more stable the film, the less is the tranfer of thermal energy. Basically, a building acquires a windchill factor on the outside surface as moving, cold air continues to remove this protective interface. Thus, recessed windows, projecting fins, and other architectural or applied devices that can preserve the external thin air film will reduce energy loss from the building.

Ordinary window screen will tend to reduce wintertime building energy losses through glazed areas but will also reduce solar radiation transmission. In selecting exterior materials, a textured rather than a slick, smooth surface will tend to reduce the building's energy loss.

Chapter 6

Interiors

As home construction nears completion, interior finishing takes place. In painting and finishing the interior as well as in selecting floor coverings, wall treatments, furniture, window coverings, equipment and accessories, careful thought should be given to every surface and material property in terms of energy and thermal- and light-reactive color, texture, and form.

Human psychoneural response should be a determining factor when considering reflectivity to work surfaces and activities that occur in the interior. Shiny, specular (mirror-like) surfaces have a glare factor that can be visually uncomfortable. Mat-finish, pure white can have a high level of reflectivity with reasonably acceptable comfort.

Use modulated color values for visual quietness, high reflectivity for stimulation and demanding visual tasks, and deep, dark colors for thermal-energy absorption, visual accent, or a lowered threshold of response (when an entire room is deepened in color). All intense, light, bright colors and high visual contrasts are stimulating.

Daylighting

Light-colored or specular-reflective furni-ture and furnishings will reflect daylight more deeply into interior space. Interior paint colors are critical for optimal reflection of daylight that penetrates windows, clerestories, or skylights. Visual adaptation and accommodation must be considered for visual tasks and comfort. Remember that external reflectivity and time-of-day changes of the sun path will affect interior daylighting characteristics. In most cases, the ceiling provides the best opportunity for in-depth daylighting and therefore should be white or very light in color. Sidewall paint tones should be carefully evaluated for the degree of reflection desired. Deeper colors over drywall or plaster will absorb indirect solar-thermal energy. Wood paneling acts as an insulator, is less desirable for passive solar homes, and is much more expensive. Keep in mind that daylighting is most effective for visual tasks when it is horizontal (lateral) in direction and at right angles to the line of vision. In all cases, surface glare should be avoided. Furniture and furnishings can reflect, absorb, or shade the flow of daylight through the interior. Painting doors a high-gloss, reflective white will allow them to be used as light reflectors between room spaces. Window coverings or treatments should not impede daylighting or direct sun to passive solar spaces. Paint colors in sunspaces must be considered in terms of thermal absorption and desired reflectivity and secondary thermal gains to adjoining spaces with adequate control over glare.

Walls and Floors

The most common, practical, and economic material that provides some fire resistance and can be painted or papered in any manner is drywall. Keep in mind, however, that paneling, wallpaper, or wall coverings add considerably to interior-finish cost. Using drywall without baseboards or door trim and with flush door jamb treatments may not cost less but reduces cleaning through the lifetime of the building.

Aggregate concrete used for thermal mass floors in sunspaces, coated with a dark, dull, mat finish such as masonry paint or concrete stain is a minimal-cost finish that can also apply to thermal walls. (Thermal mass walls do not need as much darkness in tone to perform well under direct solar exposure.) Tile, brick, or other masonry materials applied to concrete are vastly more expensive. A finished wood floor is more costly than wall-to-wall carpeting applied over a plywood (exterior grade to minimize formaldehyde) or (with on-grade adhesive) concrete slab subfloor. Keep rugs and mats off thermal mass floor areas. They prevent long-term thermal storage by their insulative properties. Wall hangings and pictures should not be placed on thermal mass walls. Keep plants from shading thermal-storage elements.

Furniture and Furnishings

Americans would do well to examine the diminutive living style, furniture, and interior arrangements of other nations. Small-scale, portable, foldable, and stacking furniture converves space and increases the multiple uses of interior rooms. Small-scale homes demand small-scale furniture. Seating pieces do not have to sacrifice comfort to size.

The more that people live close to the floor with frugal amounts of furniture, the more that can be hung on walls or put away in closets or other storage spaces and the more that a small room appears larger and becomes more useful. Provisions for healthy body posture and positions should always be considered, something that is most often ignored in Western furniture design. Many of our seating pieces distress the human back, impair our circulatory systems, and immobilize our muscles.

New Scandinavian posture-dynamic seating pieces that more efficiently support the body in balanced positions require less space and appear less obtrusive. They are expensive, but most likely their simplicity will be "knocked off" in low-cost copies. A prevailing question is always how to support the back for upright activities. Not only can these Scandinavian posture pieces be ef-

fective, but walls, low partitions, or other vertical supportive surfaces can be used with contour posture cushions designed to support the spine and posterior tissues. Ledges at the proper height can also be used for support in standing or near-standing positions.

Most seating and other furniture pieces should be light in weight and easily movable for use in multifunctional ways. Chairs can be borrowed from dining or other areas for living room conversation or recreation room purposes, or the total inventory of small side chairs can be used to increase the seating for dining. Stacking chairs, stacking cushions, and other furniture pieces that can be stored in this manner (such as small tables) can free up space for other activities. Chairs and sofas in particular should be regarded as insulators, ventilators, or heat exchangers for the human body: In cold weather, a chair or sofa with deep upholstery you can sink in is warmer; in warm weather, a chair or sofa of open webbing, mesh, rattan, or other weaves will ventilate the body. In the heat of summer or in a hot sunspace at any time, a well-ventilated or highly conductive (metal or plastic) seating piece with a configured-wire surface can cool the body as body heat is conducted to the piece and to the air. Patio furniture can also be used indoors.

Furniture for reclining positions is in contrast to that designed for the erect body. The Japanese historically solved this problem with the lightweight, movable, and foldable futon. Body comfort is assured, and the entire sleeping pad can be instantly removed, hung on a wall, folded and stacked against a wall, or put in a closet. Ordinary mattresses without box springs or water beds can also be located directly on the

floor. Inexpensive polystyrene beadboard placed under the mattress will insulate it from a cold floor. The more rigid surface of the floor and a firm mattress is better support for most backs, except for the self-modulating support of a water mattress. For those who prefer a raised bed, a box frame or platform (with or without storage drawers) can be readily constructed to support the water bed or mattress. Water mattresses left flat on the floor will not impede the visual scale of the room, but cannot be used for seating unless multicompartmented.

Furniture can be designed for efficient use of compact space. In particular, there can be stacked bunk beds; beds that hinge upward against or into walls; storage elements suspended in upper space; high, vertical chests for clothes, linens, and other household goods; low chests in closets for storage that leave hanging space above; and, upper-wall cabinets. When you want drawers, inexpensive wood chests or interlocking, plastic drawer units can be used. These units can be stacked under closet-hung clothing or disposed within the room. A unique advantage is that they can be vertically or horizontally rearranged or placed back-to-back for optimum space use. They can also be used for under-bed storage when appropriate. Inexpensive lamps are available. The old Shaker tradition of continuous rails about 6 feet (1.8 meters) above the floor with rhythmically spaced pegs used to hold clothing and other items can be adopted.

Dining can be a simple matter of need or an exercise in gastronomics. In any case, for a single, couple, or foursome the space need not exceed a 6-foot (1.8 meter) square. Small-scale metal frame, plastic, or wood chairs are needed to stay within this dining boundary. The table need not exceed a 32-inch (81.3 centimeter) square or a 36-inch (91.4 centimeter) circle. The Japanese have a just-above-floor-level table with a square hole in the floor to accommodate feet and legs. This concept avoids the need for chairs (cushions are used on the floor) and doesn't infringe upon the spatial volume of the room.

Keep in mind that furniture in sunspaces receiving direct solar radiation should create the least shadow possible and be very open and highly reflective to allow the passage of sunlight and its reflection toward a thermal mass floor, wall, or storage medium. Or, the furniture itself can possess a useful thermal mass and be placed in the sun path.

Window Treatments and Coverings

As mentioned earlier in Chapter 4, conventional draperies are a poor choice for window treatments. In addition to their heat loss problems, draperies are usually cumbersome and are difficult to provide with stacking space. They require maintenance, cleaning, and are relatively expensive if durable fabrics are used. They are subject to fading and collecting dust. They do, however, improve acoustics.

The appearance of drapes is questionable, weighed against the clean and practical lines of vertical blinds that require much less stacking room and provide a better, graduated control over daylight. Horizontal blinds collect more dust and interfere more with view but, if reflective, can direct daylight deeper into the room. Such blinds are available with a specular chrome surface on one side and a solar, heat-absorbing black on the other. Thus, summer or other unwanted solar radiation can be reflected back through the glass or the black, heat-absorbing side can act as an air-type solar collector. These blinds avoid the side-stacking problem at windows. Both drapes and blinds require a person or a mechanism to operate them at the appropriate times.

Drapes and blinds are not an equal thermal substitute for movable insulation. The advantages and disadvantages of movable insulation were covered earlier, in Chapter 4, along with strategies for reducing or eliminating its use. The basic problem with movable insulation — as with drapes and blinds — is that someone (or some mechanism) must operate it at the appropriate times; it also has a relatively high initial cost. In any case, whatever window coverings or treatments are chosen, particular care should be taken that direct sun to passive solar spaces and daylighting are not impeded. Privacy and ventilation with any type of window treatment should also not be neglected.

Kitchens

One of the major costs in equipping a kitchen — excluding large appliances — is cabinets. Cabinets come in all different types, sizes, designs, and cost ranges. In general, the more detailed the functional features, and the higher the quality, the greater the cost. Comparison shopping is recommended: Compare cost versus functional benefits. The simpler the design and details, the easier it is to clean and maintain surfaces. Flush, contemporary cabinets fit this description.

Unfortunately, no cabinet manufacturer makes standard, 30-inch (76 centimeter) deep, lower-cabinet units. The advantage of extra depth is increased countertop space and storage. Greater depth allows more countertop space for small appliances such as a toaster or convection or microwave ovens that help avoid the use of larger ovens and thereby provide more effective counter work space. When using extra-deep base cabinets, the upper units should be installed at a lower, more convenient level. Owners with adequate workshop ability might produce their own cabinets. Top surfaces can be tile or plastic laminate applied with contact cement; or, countertops can be fabricated in a shop. To increase accessibility of under-the-counter units, inexpensive, standard lazy Susans should be used on lower shelves. Where a separate pantry space is provided, dishes can be stored there to prevent overload of the regular cabinet lineup.

The most economical and practical lighting for a kitchen is surface-mounted, shielded, fluorescent ceiling fixtures. Take care to locate the fixtures so countertops are adequately illuminated. Placing lighting under upper cabinets adds to cost, although small, fluorescent strip lights that are applied with an adhesive or are screw-mounted can be relatively inexpensive and provide good task lighting. Less-efficient incandescent lighting fixtures should not be used until new, high-efficiency lamps become available.

Appliances

Appliances and equipment should be most energy efficient. Compare the Energyguide labels on major appliances to determine the amount of energy usage and the estimated annual energy cost. Carefully consider your own requirements when choosing electrical appliances, and evaluate other alternatives. Some manual devices can substitute for powered ones. If air conditioning is a need, central systems are preferred, especially heat pumps. Through-the-wall or window air-conditioners are not recommended because of their noise, intensity of air flow, and lower operating efficiency. Use standard vent diverters to capture heat and moisture from clothes dryers in the winter.

Bathrooms

At the turn of the century, most homes were accommodated by a one- or two-holed outdoor privy. A chamber pot under the bed and a nightstand with a pitcher of water were welcome indoor accessories. Through the early 1900s, a single, indoor bathroom (without a shower) was a hedonistic luxury, despite the size of the family. Four, eight, or more individuals enjoyed the physical delight of the indoor tub, toilet, and/or washbasin.

Aside from the kitchen, the modern, indoor bathroom is the most expensive room in the house. Thus, the route to affordability is to have a well-appointed, minimal bathroom or bathrooms. The best attitude for an affordable mind is to treat each addition of a lavatory, bath compartmentalization, half bath, or full bath as an added luxury. A tub-shower combination or prefabricated shower with a shower curtain is less expensive than with a glass door. Tiling in a bathroom can be particularly expensive unless you do it yourself. A small, built-in bathroom heater can save energy by providing a warm spot

in the house while leaving other indoor-space temperatures lower in cold weather.

Unfortunately, ventaway toilets that convey odors from the toilet bowl directly through the plumbing vent stack are expensive; they are the most effective means for energy-conserving odor removal. The author uses vertical-stack, 6-inch (15 centimeter) diameter wind turbines with tight-fitting manual dampers in a reachable, 7-foot (2.1 meter) high ceiling to avoid the noise and energy use of powered bathroom-exhaust fans. Bathrooms, whether internal or peripheral within the plan layout, will be more energy efficient and less costly without an outside window in cold and temperate climates. Internal, recirculating filtration fans that do not vent air to the outside are approved by some building codes, but the buildup of internal humidity in the bathroom can injure some materials. These fans will not remove the mist from a steaming shower.

Locating washers and dryers within a bathroom can save space and money. Stacking them saves even more space. In all cases, a conscious effort has been made in the presented plans to concentrate the plumbing of baths, kitchens, and utility needs together.

Control Over Noise

As human density in housing increases, noise becomes a predominant issue. People in close proximity with other people and motor vehicles tend to generate excessive noise. Highway, aircraft, and industrial noises can also be a problem. Yards, patios, other outdoor spaces, and summertime windows are open to noise intrusion. Open bedroom windows are particularly vulnerable. Tightly

constructed, well-insulated, double-glazed homes, however, act as effective shields against external noise when they are closed up.

Attached housing, duplexes, and all other side-by-side or stacked forms of living remind us that there is no substitute for good neighbors. Nevertheless, effective, affordable sound barriers need to be placed between human occupancies. Sounds within interior space are attenuated by absorption into soft or heavily textured materials. External sounds can be excluded by heavy insulation, heavy mass, and avoidance of exterior wall openings and sound-conductive materials. Walls between adjacent occupancies can be double-frame construction, tightly caulked, with batts of insulation woven between the studs so that sound vibrations are not transmitted through the wall. Various types of sound-deadening board can be installed under the drywall. Always follow manufacturer's instructions.

Heavy masonry or concrete mass walls can be installed between occupancies, but lightweight concrete blocks are not satisfactory unless their porous surface is filled in with a cementitious slurry or plaster. Check the sound transmission class (STC)[42] (decibel-reduction) rating of all occupancy wall separations when considering the level of quietness desired between such spaces. In all cases, cracks at the floor, ceiling, or within the wall must be tightly sealed with nonshrinking caulk.

Floors between occupancies pose special acoustical problems not only because of airborne noise and other sounds but because of the tapping of footsteps on an

[42]*Sweet's Catalog File: Products for General Building* (New York: McGraw-Hill Book Co., 1982), pp. 24, 49.

upper floor. Heavy carpet and pad on upper floors circumvent the annoyance of wood, vinyl, or other hard-surfaced floor coverings. Beyond this measure, sound-deadening board under any flooring material is an inexpensive procedure. Suspended ceilings and/or the interposition of acoustical materials can secure a higher level of sound attenuation.

With attached dwellings, planning and design should abate not only interior sound intrusion but also sound carrying from one occupancy to another through window or vent openings. Particular attention should be given to prevent sound intrusion from living areas to sleeping areas.

New subdivision developers and builders should establish noise abatement regulations for any development, especially those in which higher-density living is planned.

Air Pollution and Indoor Air Quality

As houses are made smaller and tighter, the amount of breathable air per person is greatly reduced. This results in a greater need to bring in outdoor air for ventilation that can be seriously polluted. The activity occurring in a certain space also influences oxygen consumption that can deplete indoor oxygen levels. Adding to this problem are numerous indoor air contaminants likely to be present in a smaller air volume.

Indoor air quality relates to economics, since methods for introducing or cleaning air all possess cost factors. A number of air pollutants and contaminants are particularly difficult to remove. Only in the past few years have medical and health researchers realized the potential dangers of indoor air

pollution. The extent of the health threat is as yet undetermined; however, it is already known that the concentration of indoor pollutants can often greatly exceed outdoor levels, placing indoor air conditions far above ambient pollution standards. The fact that most people spend up to 90 percent of their time indoors underscores the magnitude of the problem.

This section will review some of the more common types and sources of indoor air contamination and give ways of combatting the problem.

Smoking. Smoking is counter to an affordable life-style. Not only is the cost of cigarettes, cigar, or pipe an initial expense, but the maintenance, injury to possessions, surface contamination clean-up, and medical expenses further deplete the budget. Smoking is the number-one indoor air pollutant. Because the indoor air volume in a compact home is relatively small, smoking or other contaminants are especially injurious to body and environment. Smokers should go outdoors and smoke or do so in a highly ventilated space that can be closed off from the rest of the house. No-smoking signs are the most cost-effective control measure. Places where smoking is permitted require six to nine times more energy for adequate ventilation and air tempering than if it were eliminated.

Formaldehyde. One pollutant that has received a great deal of attention is formaldehyde. Formaldehyde is a construction adhesive and bonding agent, a fungicide, and a preservative. Over 6 billion pounds (2.7 billion kilograms) are produced yearly. Formaldehyde is found in plywood, particle board, carpet backing, and many other materials.

Formaldehyde causes eye and skin irritation, upper respiratory problems, headaches, dizziness, nausea, and fainting. It is suspected of causing nasal-passage cancer.

Radon gas. Radioactive radon gas may be the most dangerous component of indoor air. Radon is a naturally occurring element with unstable nuclei, created by the disintegration of radium. Radon "daughters" are radon-decay products produced by a chain or succession of nuclei disintegrations. Radon gas is present in soil gases and enters homes through unpaved basements and crawl spaces and through wet and porous structural material. Also, building materials containing radium-226 (usually masonry) and dissolved radon in well water contribute to indoor radon concentrations.

Radon-gas and radon-daughter molecules attach to tobacco smoke and other airborne particles that are then inhaled into the lungs and adhere to the bronchi. Lung tissue then receives a dose of alpha radiation, which causes lung cancer. Clear symptoms of damage caused by deposition of radon in the lungs may show up ten to forty years later.

Gas-Fired or Petroleum-Fueled Appliances and Indoor Combustion. Another major source of indoor air pollution comes from the indoor combustion of gas stoves, furnaces, dryers, and water heaters; fireplaces and stoves; and unvented kerosene space heaters. These devices produce carbon monoxide, nitrogen dioxide, formaldehyde, hydrogen cyanide, water-soluble sulfate, and respirable particles — often in concentrations that exceed outdoor-air-quality standards. Indoor combustion emissions cause respiratory ailments and decreased lung volume.

Household Products. The number of chemical products developed for use in the home is startling. Many of these household maintenance products release toxic vapors that are extremely hazardous. Some of the common household products that are potential indoor pollutants include:

- cleaning agents
- mothballs
- furniture and shoe polishes, waxes, petrochemical-based materials and solvents
- chlorine bleach
- insecticides, antifungicides, mold inhibitors
- paint, varnish, paint stripper, paint thinner, turpentine, lacquers
- aerosol sprays
- art and hobby materials
- room deodorizers, other deodorants
- nail polish and nail-polish remover
- lighter fluid, charcoal fire starter

Solutions

As discouraging as all of the above may seem, there are ways to reduce and/or eliminate indoor air contaminants in tightly constructed homes. They are discussed in the following material.

Ventilation and Filtration. Most indoor air pollution problems can generally be substantially controlled by providing good ventilation. A serious question, however, is how to meet the needs of indoor ventilation without bringing inside unacceptable outdoor pollution. First of all, avoid, if possible, heavily polluted urban areas. Select a home site away from heavily traveled roadways and industrial contamination.

Selective filtration systems can help if they are designed to capture or neutralize offending airborne particles and gases. Systems are now available that can remove harmful gases and solvents, pollen, dust, particles, and other pollutants.

In most climates, outdoor air at temperatures between 55° and 75°F (12.8° and 23.9°C) is appropriate for natural ventilation. Such temperatures occur day or night. In climates where daytime temperatures may be uncomfortably hot, nighttime temperatures can be in the comfort range. Wind and inductive (temperature differential) ventilation and cooling can be readily accomplished with correct architectural design during day hours, augmented by the sun, nighttime-stored solar heat, earth temperatures, and evaporation.

During the winter, when houses are tightly sealed, indoor smoking should be absolutely forbidden.

Plants. Indoor plants will happily absorb carbon dioxide, respire water vapor into the air, and produce small quantities of oxygen. Plants also remove impurities from the air by trapping particles on their leaves, branches, and stems and absorbing many gaseous and other pollutants directly into their leaves. This air filtration process aids indoor air quality, and the plants improve the aesthetics of the indoor environment. In a very tight home, a large number of plants could raise indoor humidity to uncomfortable levels, although some additional humidity in winter will improve comfort at lower heating temperatures.

Outgassing. The characteristics of materials, substances, and chemicals initially and over time to give off fumes, vapors, and odors is known as "outgassing." It is inevitably accelerated by heat. In particular,

certain surfaces in passive solar homes exposed to direct heat of the sun will outgas at an increased rate. While outgassing increases probable harm to human health, this has a brighter side if a sunspace has been designed for optimal ventilation and can be closed off from interior living spaces and be used as an outgassing chamber.

For several years the author has been outgassing furniture, cabinetwork, furnishings, clothing, books, plastic products, and other objects and items found in a home in his ventilated sunspace before allowing them to be placed in living or sleeping spaces. Before moving the items into your breathing space, be sure no trace of odor exists. One's own nose or someone else with a supersensitive nose can detect minute odors.

Materials Selection. Being careful about what products or items are brought into a home can help alleviate indoor pollution. Avoid buying objects, substances, or cleaning materials, or using paints, finishes, or art-and-craft supplies, etc. that exhibit strong or traceable odors or have known harmful properties. Paints, wallpapers, adhesives, and solvents that contain harmful ingredients or give evidence of serious outgassing should be avoided. Furniture and other objects should be painted outdoors. Paint indoors only during warm weather to allow for full ventilation. If possible, stay out of the house until the odors have largely subsided.

A primary concern in the design and specification of the affordable home should be to avoid and control radioactivity. Earth, stone, brick, concrete, sand, and gravel can be radioactive. Know where construction materials likely to be radioactive come from. If in doubt, have your materials checked by a laboratory with a scintillometer. Radon levels can be tested: A California company is marketing radon monitors that are placed in the house for three months and then returned to the company for analysis (Terradex Corporation, 460 North Wiget Lane, Walnut Lane, California, 94598).[43] The analysis is in picocuries per liter; one picocurie of radon in a house is equivalent to the lung cancer risk of smoking one cigarette per day.[44] An allowable radon concentration for very tight houses is three picocuries per liter.[45] Radon levels can be reduced by sealing basement cracks (especially around plumbing fixtures), painting exposed interior concrete surfaces with an epoxy or polyurethane sealant, or by installing an airtight barrier over the earth, such as a vapor barrier or concrete floor.[46]

Another source of radioactive exposure in the home that should be avoided is ionization-type smoke detectors. These devices contain either americium-249 or radium-226, both known to be carcinogenic at low exposure levels. Smoke detectors should be the photoelectric type to avoid a possible radiation hazard.

Formaldehyde outgassing can be reduced by proper materials selection. Avoid particle board, if possible, and furniture made from it. Covering plywood with latex paint and using exterior-grade plywood indoors (which has a less volatile resin) can reduce exposure to formaldehyde.[47]

[43]"Knowing for Sure: Home Tests," *New Shelter,* vol. 3, no. 5, May-June 1982, p. 25.

[44]Ibid.

[45]William A. Shurcliff, *Air-to-Air Heat Exchangers for Houses* (Cambridge, Mass.: W.A. Shurcliff, 1981), p. 5.10.

[46]Ibid., and Lafavore, p. 22.

[47]Lafavore, p. 22.

Fumes from vehicles and stored petro-fuels can also pose a problem if allowed to drift into the living spaces of a home. This problem should be prevented through planning and design.

Negative Ionization. An ion is an atom that has lost or gained an electron, resulting in a positive or negative electrical charge. Most homes and buildings tend to decrease the amount of ions in the air. One reason is that negative ions tend to attach themselves to particles in the air, imparting a negative charge to them. The particles are then drawn to walls, floors, and other room surfaces that usually have a positive charge. Metal ducting in forced-air heating grounds out negative ions. And electrostatic air cleaners, because of their electrically charged grids, also neutralize ions and can discharge ozone.

The fact that negative ions tend to knock particles out of the air to other room surfaces can be exploited to clean up indoor air pollutants through the use of a negative ion generator. These devices are especially effective in removing cigarette smoke and will also ground out radioactive particles, reducing some of the respiratory danger. Some ion generators are equipped with positively charged collectors or come with positive-field plates to attract and capture particles from the air. Take care if you have purchased (or contemplate buying) a negative ion generator that the unit does not produce ozone (which is harmful to lungs) and that the level of ionization is not so great as to disturb rest or sleep, since negative ionization increases our levels of awareness. Ion generators use less energy to clean the air of particulates than other mechanical systems that need fans, more horsepower, ducting, etc.

Air-to-Air Heat Exchangers. Air-to-air heat exchangers are gaining increasing attention as one way of dealing with ventilation and indoor pollution problems in very tight houses. These devices are common-place in Scandinavian countries where homes are required to be shut up most of the year and have also been used in many superinsulated houses in Canada.

Air-to-air heat exchangers are designed with side-by-side ducts that have a common wall containing a heat-exchange element that can be plastic, paper, or metal. They usually have two fans, for incoming and exhaust airstreams. Heat from the outgoing, stale, house air is recovered (at varying efficiencies) and transferred to incoming, colder, fresh air. This describes winter or cold-weather operation. Air-to-air heat exchangers can also be used in the summer to cool incoming warm air by transferring heat from outgoing house air that can be below ambient air temperatures. The most common use for these devices is wintertime ventilation.

The efficiencies for air-to-air heat exchangers average around 70 to 80 percent. Thus, a possible 30-percent loss, plus the additional operational cost, could be expensive, especially for larger houses. Researchers at Lawrence Berkeley Laboratory have done cost-analysis calculations and found that, for gas-heated homes, the use of heat exchangers is not economical for most of the country. However, exchangers appear cost-effective in homes heated by electricity or oil, except in temperate regions.[48] The researchers suggest that air-

[48]"Heat Exchangers Effective in Radon Control," *Passive Solar Journal,* vol. 1, no. 1, Jan. 1982, pp. 52-53.

to-air heat exchangers may be cost-effective for control of indoor radon buildup in tight houses as outlined above.[49]

An air-to-air heat exchanger could be an expensive item for a small home. As an alternative, the author suggests using a sunspace to heat outdoor, ventilation air and being more careful about outgassing. If you decide to purchase a heat exchanger for a residence, Canadian energy researchers suggest it should have the following features:

1. The heat-recovery ratio or effectiveness should be around 70 percent or more at the design air flow.
2. In freezing climates, the unit should have a defrost cycle to automatically limit frost buildup. This is usually done by closing the outdoor, air intake duct and letting the warm, house-exhaust air melt the ice. (Unfortunately, this also stops ventilation. An alternative is to use a small, air-type solar collector to preheat the incoming air.)
3. Fan capacity should be sufficient to draw air from several points in the house through modest-sized (4-inch-[102 mm] diameter) ducts.[50]

Other Solutions. If gas-combustion appliances must be used, try to find those with pilotless ignition. Kitchen range hoods over gas stoves can reduce levels of carbon monoxide, formaldehyde, and nitrogen dioxide. They must vent to the outside, which will result in wintertime heat losses.

*

Researchers have found that to reduce the above pollutant levels to the most stringent health standards, the fans in the range hoods must be capable of a 140 cubic-feet-per-minute airflow.[51] Gas ovens can also be vented to the outside, and outside combustion air can be supplied to gas furnaces, which will save money on fuel and increase the humidity level in the house.[52]

Testing for the presence of pollutants is one way of determining if there is a serious indoor air pollution problem. If you suspect something in your home is at fault, a good first step is to open the house up and ventilate very well for a week, then close the house up for a week. If the symptoms go away and then return, this confirms something in the house is causing the problem.[53] Then more specific tests can be used to pinpoint possible sources.

There appears to be a consensus among experts and in the building industry that 0.5 air changes per hour (ACH) (one air change in the home every two hours) will keep indoor pollutants below critical levels.[54] This air-infiltration rate is comparable to what the average home owner can achieve by caulking and weather-stripping an existing home.[55] Some new homes being constructed today can have infiltration rates as low as 0.05 ACH, equivalent to one air change every 20 hours! For these and other supertight homes, special precautions and measures as described must be taken to ensure adequate ventilation and uncontaminated indoor air.

Air is the most important ingredient for the sustenance of human life. We can live for a protracted time without food or water but only for minutes without air. The quality of air relates directly to the quality of our health. Because the earth's atmosphere is so abundant, we are individually and collectively not meticulous enough about its purity. Therefore, a particular effort needs to be made to solve and control air polllution problems through design.

---

[49]Ibid.

[50]Harold Orr and Rob Dumont, "Air Tightness in Buildings," *Alternative Sources of Energy,* no. 53, Jan.-Feb. 1982, pp. 26-27.

[51]Winslow Fuller, "What's in the Air for Tightly Built Houses?" *Solar Age,* vol. 6, no. 6, June 1981, pp. 30-32.

[52]Zamm, p. 110.

[53]"Knowing for Sure," p. 25.

[54]Fuller, "What's in the Air," p. 32.

[55]Lafavore, p. 25.

Chapter 7

Conclusion

Every project should be functionally, economically, and scientifically designed to optimize the opportunities as well as the constraints of site and microclimate energies. The designs of this book are general and should not be construed as necessarily meeting the conditions of a specific home-building project. Certain cautions should be exercised.

Keep in mind that, within the requirements of year-round livability and energy use, a reasonable compromise should be made so that the project design maximizes winter solar collection but minimizes possible excessive overheating through the fall or underheating in the early spring.

As stated in the beginning, the affordable, compact, passive solar home designs presented in this book are principally designed for the larger temperate and cold-climate zones of the continental United States. While the general design principles will apply to more northerly latitudes (with greater attention to climatic extremes) more southerly hot-humid or hot-arid climatic zones have had scant attention. To facilitate a better understanding of the influence of climatic zones, a zone map and general climatic guidelines are included in the appendix.

A number-one objective of design should be livability of the architecture, site, and, particularly, interior. Most individuals spend most of their time indoors. Every attempt, however, should be made to optimize the use of outdoor space, as suggested by the plans presented in this book.

"Affordability" is open to individual interpretation. The more spacious rooms keep within the bounds of the most economic structural spans and do not greatly increase construction costs — especially of the labor required. The expensive elements of the house — namely, bathrooms and kitchens — are efficient in a minimized space. So-called luxury features and details can be either initially or in the future provided by the owner. Compact affordability does not mean an absence of aesthetic delight; in fact, a simple, low-cost design statement can have less superficiality and artifice. Gilding the lily does not make it more beautiful.

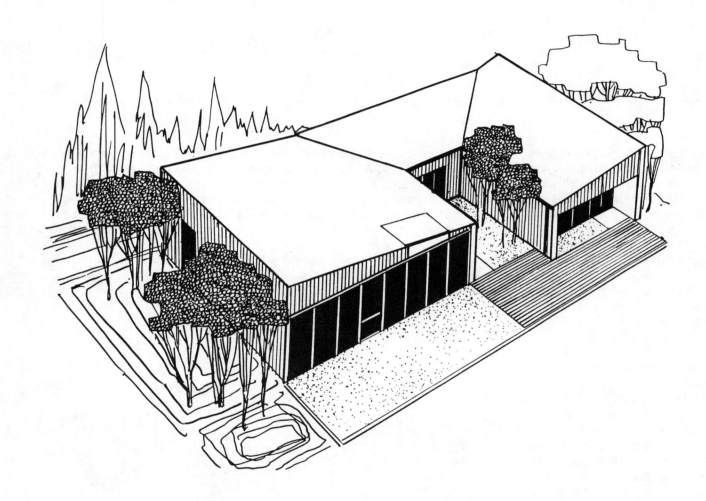

Part 2

Home Designs — Floor Plans and Characteristics

Introduction to Part 2

The perspective designs of this book are primarily conceptual, addressed to temperate and cold-climate zones. The plan drawings and sections for these affordable homes are based on a 4x4-foot (1.2x1.2-meter) module to conserve construction materials and labor. The actual working-drawing construction plans that must be prepared should be drawn to a 4-foot (1.2 meter) grid (see Compact Homes Nos. 3 and 4) to avoid detailed dimensions and act as simple reference. Multiple dwellings are at a smaller scale. The sectional drawings are composite to illustrate the solar and architectural concepts.

The drawings and descriptions are intended as a conceptual and practical guide. Every site and every project has its own unique conditions that should be met by appropriate design.

800 Square Feet (74 Square Meters)

Design

In 1975, this 800-square-foot (74-square-meter), 20x20 foot (6.1x6.1 meter), bi-level living unit was designed by the author and completed by a general contractor in five weeks within normal weekly working hours for a cost of $19,500, including air-type solar collectors. It has proven to be livable, rentable, pleasant, and adaptable. Its sophisticated simplicity has appealed to young professionals, but it could accommodate anyone who can walk up and down a flight of stairs. This house was initially designed as a prototype to take the place of mobile homes or for duplex or cluster housing. Another design version of this home is illustrated with a carport, outside storage, and awnings.

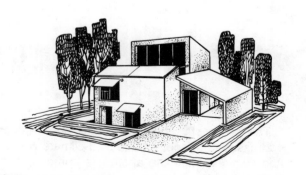

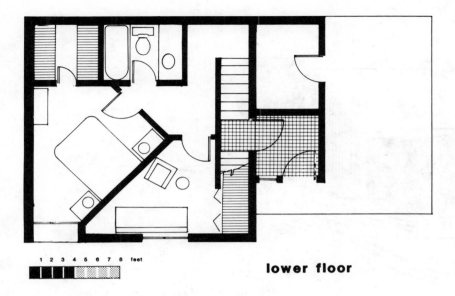

1 2 3 4 5 6 7 8 feet

lower floor

1 2 3 4 5 6 7 8 feet

upper floor

Solar

Because of its tight, urban location and a thickly branched, towering tree to the south, solar collection had to be confined mainly to the roof. The active solar roof collectors are air-type and charge a well-insulated, gravel, thermal-storage bin under the center of the house. The high, ceiling return-air duct sucks up the hottest stratified interior air and, with the solar air-handling unit, delivers it as desired to all interior spaces. The air-locked entry receives direct, passive solar winter gains as does the triangular sunspace on the upper level. The lower windows to the south also take some direct solar gain.

Ventilating and Cooling

A west-facing, solar-heated plenum assists cooling and ventilating during warm and hot weather. Air exhausts through a wind-activated roof turbine. Outdoor air enters through carefully located, small-hood, screened, close-to-the-floor, air-intake vents with insulated and weather-stripped inner doors. A sliding, outside, screened door to the sunspace aids in direct-wind cooling. A duct-distribution system with a small furnace provides supplemental heating.

Construction

This home was constructed with below-grade, pressure-treated lumber for the foundation. A treated foundation plate sets directly on a footing bed of gravel. The entire structure is of frame and was designed to avoid materials and labor waste in construction. The unit was actually covered with thick-butt hand-split cedar shakes for minimal maintenance and thermal advantage.

Features

The spacious attic behind the roof collectors has considerable storage space, but it could be a sleeping loft (if a window were added) with access by a pull-down, ceiling ladder. The diagonal bedroom partition on the lower level allows generous room for cabinets and a queen-size bed. The walk-in closet is unusual in so small a home. Another closet is placed under the stairway.

The thermal mass floor of concrete and tile in the entry and sunspace retains solar gain. A stacked washer and dryer, a relatively spacious kitchen, adaptability to furniture arrangements — these make this home a delight. Storage for books and small objects is provided in the wide, enclosed, stairway, cabinet rail.

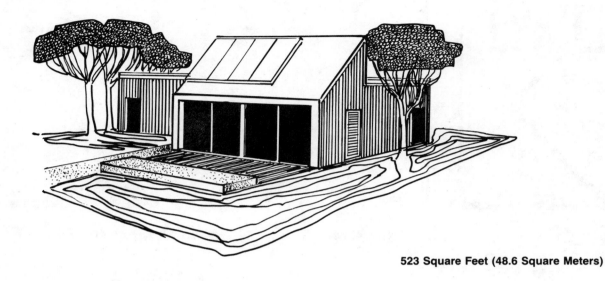

523 Square Feet (48.6 Square Meters)

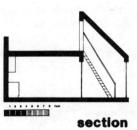

section

Design

The simple rectangular plan of this dwelling has a proportionately large sunspace. The sunspace can serve as a climatic buffer; an air-locked entry; an adaptive living space; ladder access to the larger, usable, roof deck; and as a greenhouse (plants injured by cold air should not be placed in the path of the entry doors). The main structure is only 12 feet (3.7 meters) wide. This could be a manufactured, modular unit with an add-on sunspace. The sunspace should be enticing to individuals who have solar minds and a green thumb.

The privacy and practicality of the floor plan should fit with nearly any single's or couple's use of space.

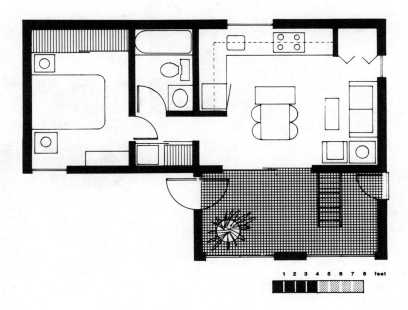

Solar

The sunspace should be appropriately glazed in accordance with solar transmissivity and climatic and internal conditions affecting cold-weather heat loss. Thermal mass in addition to the floor can be supplied with water tubes or eutectic salts. A small blower, preferably powered by photovoltaic cells, discharging solar-heated air from the sunspace into the living area is desirable. Secondary solar gains through the inner, glass side-sliding doors (which can be single glazed) should not be overlooked. The tilt angle of the roof collectors should be set for year-round domestic hot water heating. The solar tank can be placed in the upper part of the sunspace (structurally supported). Extra collector panels could provide space heat to a proper type of fan-coil unit.

Ventilating and Cooling

The sunspace can be effectively ventilated through the entry door and a louvered grille or door at the opposite end of the space. Two horizontally placed louvers with interior-insulated, weather-stripped doors can control airflow amounts. The upper air-control doors should be counterweighted. Air can flow in conventional casement windows through the sunspace, which then acts as a ventilating and cooling system. Screened patio doors can be supplied in hot and humid climates for optimal ventilation by prevailing breezes. Cooling can be further provided by evaporative stay-dry units, heat pumps, or conventional refrigerated units, depending upon climatic suitability, costs, and preferences.

Features

The kitchen area is relatively large with its pantry, and it could be reduced in size to accommodate a stacked washer and dryer. Dining could occur in the sunspace, thus allowing for more living room area. Closet provisions are generous. Some storage could be provided in the upper portion of the sunspace (along with the hot water tanks). The sunspace has room for a hot tub. The main (living, kitchen, and bedroom) living unit is 12x32 feet (3.7x9.8 meters) with the sunspace 8x16 feet (2.4x4.9 meters).

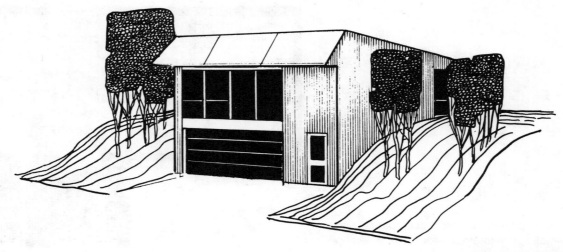

529 Square Feet (49 Square Meters)

Design

This contemporary garage house is reminiscent of carriage houses of the past. It has only a 24-foot (7.3-meter) -square foundation that supports a ground-level garage and a second-floor residence. Its square form is adaptable with a reversal or rotation of the plan to match a south solar exposure. A south-frontage solar orientation is illustrated. The stacking of residence over garage has the economy of a common roof and foundation, a minimized volume-to-surface ratio, and an arrangement for thermal efficiency. The two-car garage offers convenience and security and the upper-level living quarters have the added privacy of being above street level.

Solar

Direct passive solar gains with water or eutectic-salts thermal mass (support beam must be adequate for load) can be accomplished with the south street frontage design. Active solar collectors affixed to an angular canopy (which provides summer shade) can serve for heating domestic hot water and a portion of interior space. Very-dark-painted, south-facing garage doors (although insulated) make the garage into a nominal solar collector.

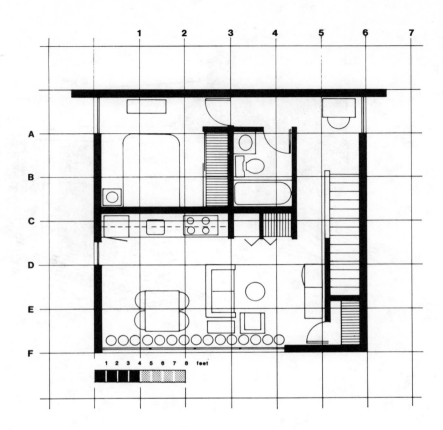

Ventilating and Cooling

Interior diagonal cross ventilation can be readily accomplished with awning-type windows and with the aid of a louvered, outer, main-entrance door at the main-floor level. A living area located on the second floor will catch more direct cooling breezes. It is important that the garage be separately ventilated to ensure the removal of gas fumes.

Features

This cube-shaped dwelling can be sheltered with earth berms and landscaping. The garage provides storage and vehicle protection. The configuration of the plan and design makes it useful for attached townhomes and condominiums. The very small lot size required makes it ideal for high-density, low-cost living. There is a psychological resistance to the prominence of the garage door, which could be located on a side opposite the stairway — if the width of the site is adequate.

549 Square Feet (51 Square Meters)

Design

This alternative garage house has a sophisticated, contemporary-design flavor. The change in the roof form, solar-ventilation plenum, and south-projecting solar-heat trap make this version somewhat more expensive to build. The southside solar orientation has a dark thermal wall for direct solar gains. The overhang shades this wall in summer.

Solar

The two-story, solar-collecting, thermal-heat-trap envelope is designed for a dark, intervening, operable blind to capture the sun's radiation and, with a duct at the high point and a blower, store the heat in a thermal mass in the garage. Heat would be withdrawn from storage as needed for the upper-level residence. The rooftop south-facing solar collectors are located to the north to reduce a probability of neighboring obstruction to the south. West-facing garage doors logically should be given a white or other light, reflective color to reduce excessive spring, summer, and fall solar heat gains.

This design will require considerable unobstructed sun from the south to function properly.

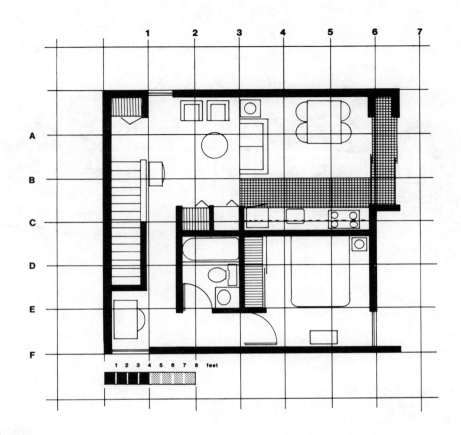

Ventilating and Cooling

This alternative design has a west-facing solar plenum, possibly with eutectic salts for thermal mass to sustain interior inductive ventilation. A reflective roof would aid cooling and improve solar impact on the collectors. Horizontal louvered grilles aligned at the end of the garage door would take in ventilation air. Removable insulative panels would cover the interior side of the openings in cold weather.

Features

This alternative plan reverses the initial plan (preceding home no. 3) to agree with view or other desires. The stairway to the north acts as a thermal buffer. Although this model does not lend itself easily to townhome attachment, offset staggering would provide an interesting complexity and privacy.

808 Square Feet (75 Square Meters)

Design

This friendly appearing, two-story dwelling has a full-length north-side storage room. It is an ideal abode for the home-loving individual or couple who like to stash everything away. This two-floor storage area plus the earth-sheltering to the north provide an effective thermal buffer. This house has a compartmented interior character for persons who like clearly defined spaces. The interior provides a very protected feeling.

Solar

The lower-level sunspace is a relatively small thermal buffer and stores solar thermal gains. It can be simply a heat-gathering space designed to connect with the upper-level, quasi-attic, where a black-painted airflow tube intercepts and delivers the sun's heat to storage in a remote rock bin (possibly at the end of the storeroom) or an underfloor gravel plenum. The attic space could take heat from the lower sunspace, and the exposed duct could act as a solar collector. Domestic hot water could be solar heated.

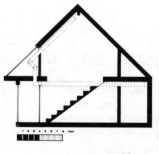

section

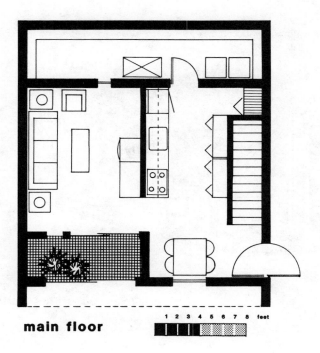

main floor

1 2 3 4 5 6 7 8 feet

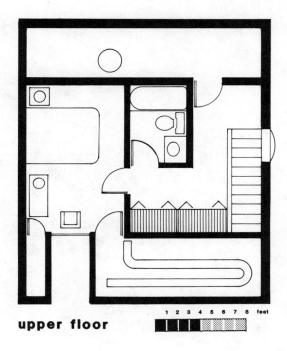

upper floor

1 2 3 4 5 6 7 8 feet

Ventilating and Cooling

Ridge-peak venting would be most appropriate. The house is earth-sheltered and, with the large thermal mass, would be cooler in summer and warmer in winter. Ventilation air traversing the earth-coupled space would be cool and improve interior comfort. Properly sized and zoned supplemental heating would benefit the compart-mentalization of the spaces.

Features

The storage room can be an extensive, provisional facility for earth-cooled home canning and relatively long-term food preservation. The washer and dryer could be located at the main-floor level in the storeroom.

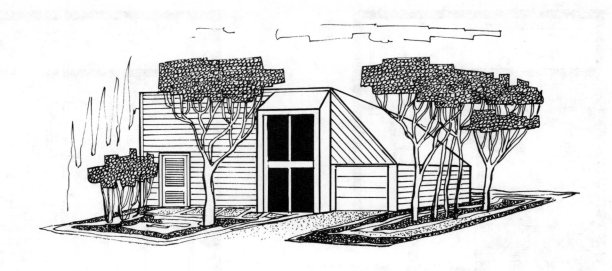

822 Square Feet (76.4 Square Meters)

Design

This compact house is illustrated with the security of an attached garage. It offers pleasant living for singles, mingles, couples, visiting relatives, and guests. The lower den has access to a bath and provides space for overflow gatherings. This design can be planned for two-family use. The upper-level sitting area may serve many uses, such as a studio, home office, television area, extra on-line kitchen, or additional sleeping space. The home would also make a good attached duplex or two-level fourplex.

Solar

This design possesses multidirectional solar-orientation capability. The area with the greatest amount of glass is assumed to be south. Various forms of solar-thermal storage, such as water tubes, selective-surface water tanks, or eutectic salts can be employed directly in front of the glazed areas. Heat-absorbing plastic or glass inner glazing can provide a thermal envelope in which heat gains can be mechanically stored in a rock bin or underfloor gravel plenum.

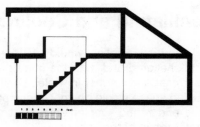

section

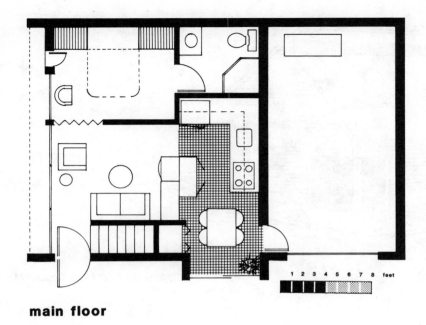

main floor

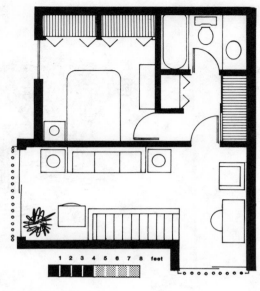

upper floor

Another option is to provide a double-back stairway along the illustrated glass area and to open the living room as well as the breakfast nook and kitchen to direct gain solar radiation with thermal-floor storage. In such a case, the garage door would face south. Another option is for the sloping roof of the garage to be oriented to the south with a relatively large array of active, air- or fluid-type solar collectors for domestic hot water and interior space heating (avoiding trees on the south). The nearly flat roof will adapt to any type of solar collectors for domestic hot water heating. Glass areas now on the north wall would have to be minimized.

Ventilating and Cooling

Windows, lower and upper patio doors with protective railings, and a louvered entry door will provide cross ventilation. Supplemental cooling could be met by heat pumps or conventional, mechanical means. Minizoning supplemental heating fits the diversities of space use.

Features

To create separate apartments, the entry could have inner doors separating upper and lower occupancies, and a kitchen could be added upstairs. Single-entry outside doors favor security. The storage in and over the attached garage could be reached by a pull-down stairway from the garage or from the second floor. The east-facing breakfast nook would be pleasant in the morning and with sliding doors provides a patio protected from the west sun. The garage could be double to serve a two-family occupancy. A basement and basement stairway are provided from the breakfast nook. Thirty-inch-deep (76-centimeter) lower kitchen cabinets, a 54-inch (137-centimeter) -high cabinet and room divider, and an adjacent work table create a spacious environment.

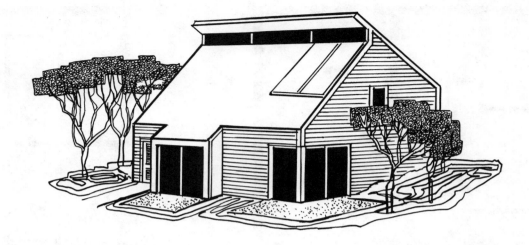

828 Square Feet (76.9 Square Meters)

Design

This home evolved into a traditional look. Its interior plan can accommodate one or two singles or couples. A basement with descending-under-ascending stairway can add space and storage. An attached garage can have access at the kitchen.

Solar

Three passive solar systems (a sunspace, a south bay with thermal mass, and a clerestory with destratification duct) can circulate heat for effective comfort. They can also provide heat that can be retained in a gravel-storage bin or plenum for heating as needed. The clerestory would have an overhead reflector to intensify winter solar radiation and provide summer shade. Active solar collectors could be used for heating domestic hot water.

section

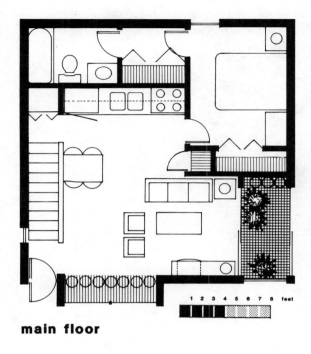

main floor

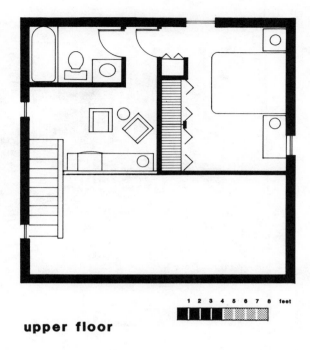

upper floor

Ventilating and Cooling

The high ceiling above the lower living space is ideal for natural ventilation. Screened side-sliding doors in the sunspace and bed-room casement windows provide ventilation and seasonal cooling. The climate might dictate a heat pump; refrigerated or evaporative cooling can be provided. Supplemental heating can be provided as needed.

Features

This plan provides for two separate seating areas and the privacy of bedrooms and baths. The kitchen could be shared. On a compact scale, it offers the cost sharing of tandem living.

The provision of a basement or garage (or both) would help meet usual storage needs for sporting goods, camping gear, and other personal possessions.

This living unit can be easily joined to a mirror image of itself. Such a duplex would gain better security, shared land costs, and a larger architectural scale.

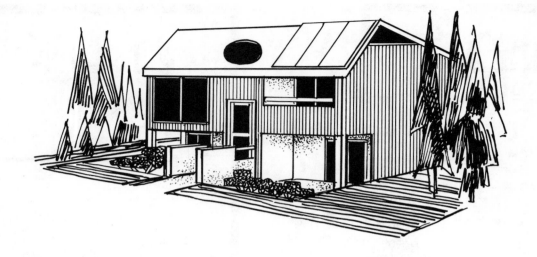

830 Square Feet (77.1 Square Meters)

Design

This home design has an appeal for home owners who enjoy outdoor living spaces. Even in a cold climate, the south-facing upper porch and lower sunken courtyards remain weather protected. This two-bedroom-and-den, bi-level plan is ideal for family living. The lower courtyard spaces that recess into the house could be initially or later closed in to act as effective passive solar sunspaces. The upper porch can also be treated in a similar manner.

Solar

Water tubes, water bunkers, or eutectic salts can store the sun's heat in the living room area. The architectural enclosures with glass, as mentioned above, would, with the living room, provide a large measure of wintertime, passive solar heat. The glass entry door allows solar heating of the interior entry space. A double-insulated, plastic roof bubble; a gable; and a triangular window will provide interior daylighting. Roof-mounted solar collectors heat domestic hot water.

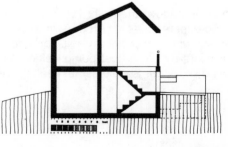

section

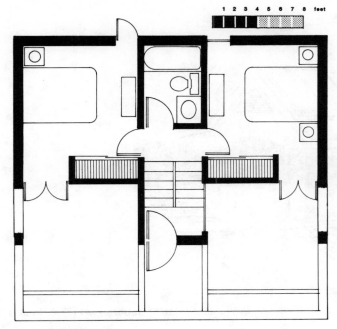

lower floor

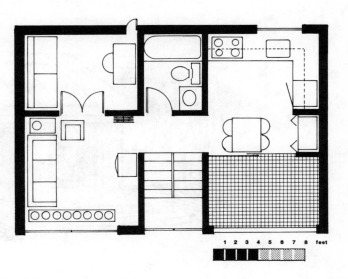

main floor

Ventilating and Cooling

Concrete foundations with lower-level, south-facing concrete walls and upper framing for the roof and exterior walls are illustrated. Downstairs bedrooms tend to remain cooler in summer and warmer in winter. Intake air through the lower-level windows will introduce cooling and ventilation and aid exhaust by natural convection through ridge-line ventilators.

Features

Bi-level homes tend to be less expensive than other types of homes, and stacked utilities also lower costs. An on-site garage would provide storage that is lacking.

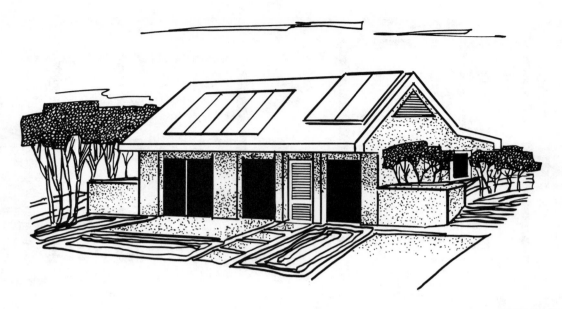

620 Square Feet (57.6 Square Meters)

Design

This earth-covered home has a pitched-roof portion that can accommodate effective solar collection. This simple plan has emphasized a spacious master bedroom and the delight of an insulated hot tub recessed into the floor. The rectangular proportion is particularly ideal for a northerly dwelling in regard to solar and climatic response.

The bath, screened from the living area by the washer-and-dryer closet, serves both bedrooms. This home is suitable for singles, mingles, couples, couples with a child, or visiting guests.

Solar

The south roof pitch would be determined to correspond with the most effective solar collection at a given latitude. An attic open to the sunspace is illustrated with eutectic salts or water in dark containers that can receive direct solar radiation. A ridge-line duct with a motorized fan should be employed to distribute the combined passive solar gains from the sunspace and living area to the various interior rooms. Delivery of the heated air should be near the floor line. Operable, lightweight insulation panels are advised for cold

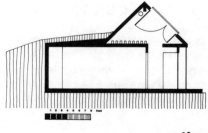

section

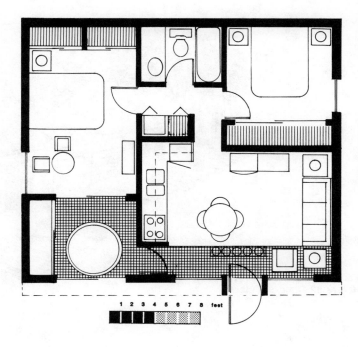

and very cold climates. These can be motor activated in response to solar collection. A thermal mass bunker in the living area should be provided to supplement the solar, thermal mass concourse that terminates in the sunspace. Active solar collectors should be sized to serve the hot tub as well as the heating of domestic hot water. If an active solar system is not provided for the hot tub, it should have a transparent plastic cover and can have fin-type water collectors in the sunspace for direct solar collection. Otherwise, the tub should have a well-insulated cover.

Ventilating and Cooling

Earth-coupling will provide summer cooling as will the earth-covered roof portion. Cross ventilation of the attic space can aid summer cooling of the sunspace, the attic thermal mass, and the interior in general. An earth tube can be provided also to cool incoming outdoor air. The louvered entry door, patio door, and windows will add to the influx of outdoor air.

Features

The master bedroom is large enough to also serve as a study, quiet TV room, or relaxed conversation room. The hot tub (unless omitted) becomes a principle feature (for passive solar storage as well). Coats can be stored in a portion of the sunspace closet, in the guest bedroom, or in the washer-dryer closet, with those appliances stacked to one side. Linen storage can be within a portion of any of the generous amount of storage spaces or on shelves over the washer and dryer. Kitchen cabinets are illustrated at a 30-inch (76-centimeter) depth.

**441 Square Feet/882 Square Feet Attached
(41 Square Meters/82 Square Meters)**

Design

This compact residence can be individually constructed or joined by the attachment of garages. Separation of the units by the garages creates more privacy for each unit. It also increases the visible scale of the architecture while concealing the automobiles and sundry other items. The diagonal and central placement of the bathroom clearly defines living, dining, kitchen, and bedroom spaces. It also, with its interior diagonal partitions, gives a feeling of greater dimension to each room space. A single or a couple could be right at home in this small abode.

Solar

The pyramidal form of the roof allows a southern street access to the front or either side of this dwelling. The plan also can be rotated or flipped over so that a north street access can have an entry from the side but have passive solar living and dining spaces as well as active solar domestic hot water collection facing south to the rear of the dwelling. Thus an entry and living and dining areas to the north can be avoided in temperate and cold climates. Northside living spaces that seek to avoid direct solar gains can be desired for hot southern climates. A thermal mass wall can enclose the bathroom and hot rooftop air can be destratified into this space. Most people enjoy a warm bathroom and centralization of heat, including solar gains, can be a benefit.

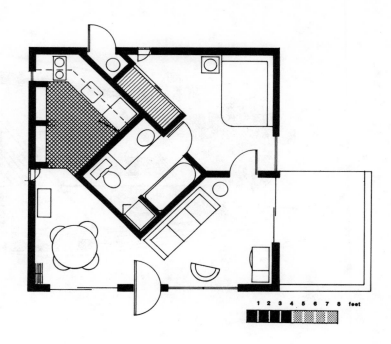

1 2 3 4 5 6 7 8 feet

Ventilating and Cooling

The peak of the pyramid roof stack (or belvedere) can be used to assist ventilation and cooling. Peripheral glass sliding doors, a louvered-door entry, and a through-the-wall northside operable, hooded, or louvered vent can provide intake air. The higher the central stack and the upper portion of the roof that forms a solar-heated plenum, the greater will be the inductive airflow. Roof overhangs should be proportional to climate. The bathroom can have a roof-turbine vent with a manual ceiling damper to decrease energy loss.

Features

A loft with ladder access for storage, sleeping, or whatever (with an operable, angled roof window) can assist practical need. Pyramid power may also be a supernatural bonus. Access from the outside to a small space is provided. The patio doors can expand the dining and living areas for outdoor living. A generous pantry and cupboard is available in the kitchen. The stacked washer-dryer in the bath is practical and expands the size of the bath.

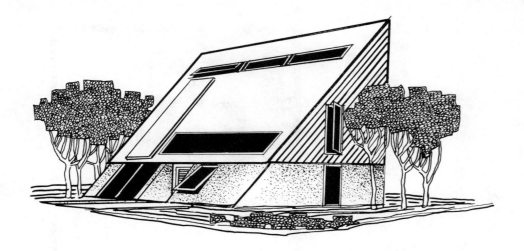

645 Square Feet (60 Square Meters)

Design

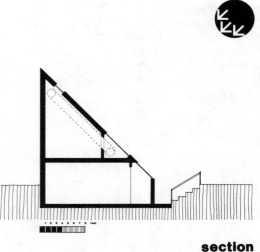

The triangle is a strong visual and structural shape that favors interseasonal solar collection as well as inductive ventilation. This earth-coupled, very livable two-bedroom/two-bath habitat offers a high-ceilinged living space, sunspace, and a generous dining area. The family with one or two children of the same sex, older adults with visiting children, two couples (rather crowded), or mingles could enjoy this low-maintenance home. With the relocation of east-facing windows to the north wall (triple-glazed or with Heat Mirror in cold climates), these living units can be continued as low-cost condominiums or townhomes.

section

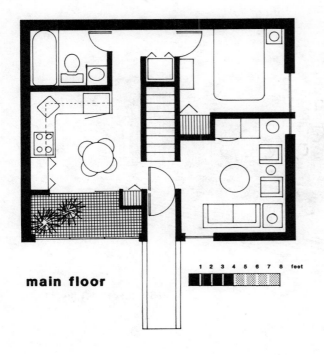

main floor

upper floor

Solar

A three-element hybrid solar system collects the sun's rays within the south-facing sunspace, an intervening solar plenum, and through a bank of clerestory windows at the apex of the roof. All internal heat loads would likewise be collected at the interior apex. Heat from flat-black, lateral, round ducts exposed to direct solar radiation and from equipment, appliances, lights, and people could be circulated by a blower through the entire interior space or be relocated to an underfloor thermal-heat-storage plenum. Slots at the periphery of the plenum would be provided for return air. Flat-plate solar collectors or a very large single collector could be employed for heating domestic hot water.

Ventilating and Cooling

The hybrid solar system could be used during warm and hot weather to either inductively or mechanically cool and ventilate when outdoor temperatures are moderate. Ventilation can be provided by screened, casement windows and the main-entry, screened, louvered door. Supplemental heating can be used as needed.

Features

Although this house is very small, it offers the privacy of separate bedrooms on two floors. The front sunken patio can be enlarged for functional, outdoor use. A pantry is provided in the kitchen. The large southern roof area would be ideal for photovoltaic power for partial or full operation of the interior electrical equipment.

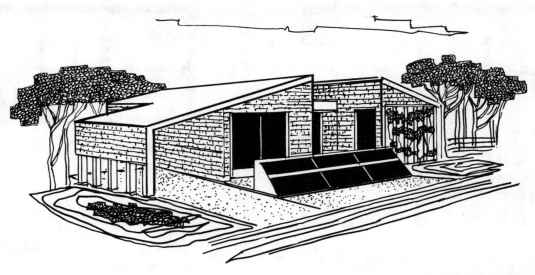

698 Square Feet (64.8 Square Meters)

Design

This plan is designed for manufactured housing. Two 12 x 24-foot (3.7 x 7.3-meter) modular units, formed on site by a connecting center section, constitute this dwelling. An extension of the roof (as illustrated) can produce a shed-like carport. The centralized sun deck and sunspace provide a focal setting and protected wintertime place for outdoor or indoor solar stimulation.

Although compact in plan, it offers generous and clearly defined spaces for living, dining, and sleeping. Doors can be widened to 36 inches (91.4 centimeters) for senior citizens and the handicapped with wheelchairs. Exterior ramps can be provided to the central sun deck.

Solar

Water tubes or eutectic salts in a cabinet designed for efficient thermal function are the principal mass for retention of the sun's energy. Self-contained thermosiphon collectors mounted at ground level to the south would heat domestic hot water.

Solar thermal gains from the sunspace and clerestory are transported by a duct and blower fan to underfloor rock-bin storage.

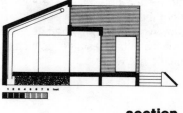

section

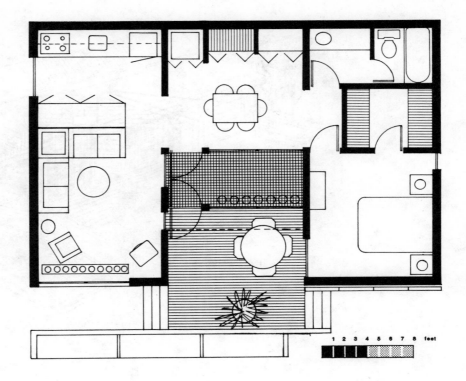

Ventilating and Cooling

Each modular section can be most expeditiously treated as a separate space-ventilating problem. Casement windows and a screened, louvered, ventilating entry door can be used for moderate-temperature nighttime or daytime cooling. Roof wind turbines or other more efficient roof ventilation configurations can be used for roof exhausts. They should have manual or electrically operated tight-fitting dampers. Power should not be required to hold them open but for their remote-control operation.

Features

The walk-in bedroom closet is generous in size. This house has abundant cabinetwork, including 30-inch (76-centimeter) -deep kitchen base cabinets. Provisions are made for a stacked washer and dryer. Plumbing is in line. All light switches can be lowered to 36 inches (91.4 centimeters) and convenience outlets raised to 18 inches (45.7 centimeters) from the floor for the handicapped. Door hardware is set at 32 inches (81.3 centimeters) from the floor.

B

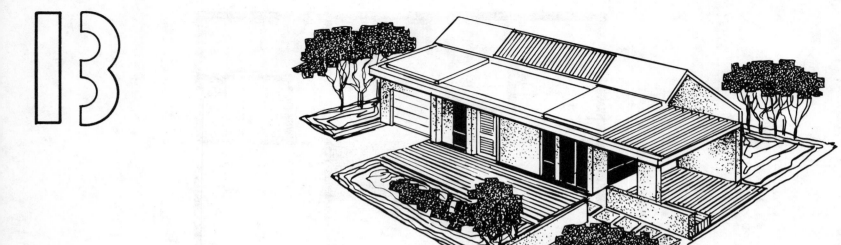

670 Square Feet (62.2 Square Meters)

Design

This low-profile home is one of the few in this book with an attached garage. Garages are particularly important as places of storage and this one, with an automatic door opener and direct inside access to the house, offers greater physical security. However, this house is designed to accommodate an unusual amount of storage with attic space (with ladder access) and a storeroom off the sunspace that could be converted to a den, hobby room, workshop, or home office. This dwelling would be ideal for a couple or a creative single.

Solar

The relatively large sunspace with a dark mass floor can benefit by additional water tube or eutectic-salt thermal mass. The sunspace is also large enough to be used as a food-raising greenhouse with the rear storage space that could be a potting room, place for raising sprouts, and/or for the use of hydroponic equipment.

The raised portion of the roof can use evacuated-tube solar collectors for heating domestic water or contribute to interior space heating by extending the collectors the full length of the roof. If south might be to the rear of the house, the collectors could simply be located on the roof slope facing south. In climates without snow, Harold Hay's patented Skytherm South roof pond system could be used over the living and dining areas for solar heating and nocturnal clear-sky cooling. For concept engineering information, see references.

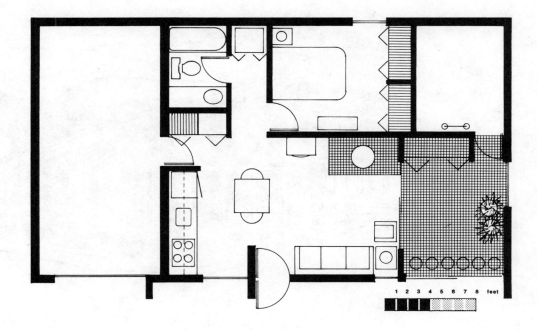

Ventilating and Cooling

The east patio is shaded by the house itself late in the day as well as by the overhead wood trellis. The sunspace is ventilated and cooled by a side-sliding patio door either to the south (as shown on the plan) or east, with a fixed-glass and low-awning window to the south (as shown on the perspective). Exhaust ventilation can be best accomplished at the high point of the roof by inductive ventilation or powered systems tailored to climatic needs. A climatically proportioned roof overhang will aid summer cooling.

Features

The south-facing entrance door lessens the need for an air-locked entry. Provision is made for a solid-fuel stove or liquid- or gas-fueled space heater. Outside combustion air should be provided by an insulated duct under the floor. It should be noted that this plan requires a fairly wide site to accommodate the garage and for adequate passive solar access when the south face is not at the street frontage.

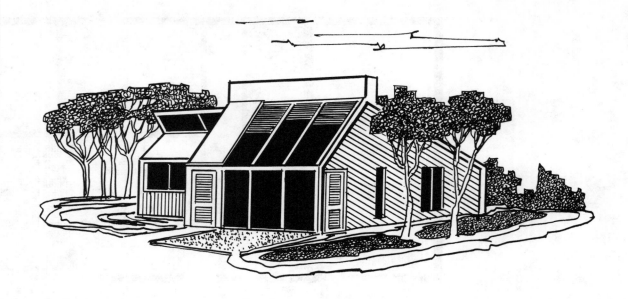

725 Square Feet (67.4 Square Meters)

Design

Sloping glass used for architecture is always attractive but often impractical in energy terms. The sloping-glass roof on this sunspace has the negative value of solar overheating and excessive clear-sky cooling. However, with some (expensive) form of movable insulation, heat losses can be reasonably controlled. This single-floor plan layout with a bedroom and a den (which can be used as a small second bedroom) has a spacious feeling for so small a living unit. This plan and design has many advantages for comfort and use. It provides some ideal features for nearly any type of buyer. Its principal lack is storage, which could be supplied by attaching a large garage.

Solar

As a money-saving alternative, the sloping roof of the sunspace can simply be framed in and insulated well. Other alternatives are double-glazed, clear-plastic skylights with movable insulation. In high-density developments where winter sun cannot enter vertical glazing, roof glazing is the next possible option.

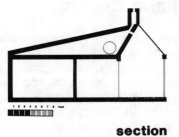

section

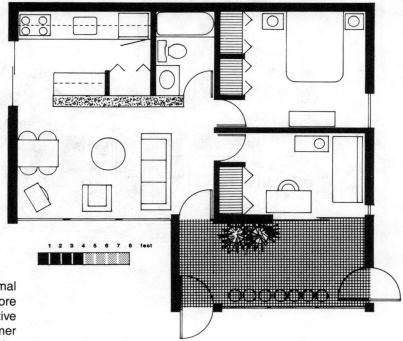

A concrete or masonry inner thermal mass wall plus a thermal mass floor with water tubes, water bunkers, or eutectic salts store solar energy. An additional passive solar system uses a reflective roof; a tilted clerestory window (to achieve architectural summer shading); and a masonry thermal mass wall centralized within the interior. Bunker-type thermal mass storage can also be used with southside glazing at the living room area. Thermosiphon or other active solar systems can be placed on the sloping roof of the sunspace. The den would receive secondary solar gains.

Ventilating and Cooling

The roof-ridge thermal plenum increases inductive-ventilation airflows with solar heat. This plenum would need dampered exhaust ports that could be manually or automatically activated with or without electric power. Screened air-intake louvers, doors, windows, a patio door, and through-the-wall vents cool and ventilate the living room. Nocturnal pressurized cooling (rather than attic-exhaust fans) can be effective using the filtered intake of outdoor air. (Locate the fans in space that is unoccupied at night because of the large cubic-feet-per-minute airflow.) Depending on climatic characteristics, other mechanical cooling, heat pumps, or conventional, refrigerated cooling can be used.

Features

This living unit can accommodate an attached garage opening to the south or west ahead of the living room with a door from the sunspace. The plan can also be flipped over so that the garage door opens south or east, which is better than facing it west and overheating it!

In colder climates, a portion of the sunspace can become an air-locked entry with either glass or a thermal wall separating the entry from the sunspace. This home would be very luminous and sunny with interior daylighting.

The hot water tank for supplemental solar heating could, with structural provisions, be located in the attic. Extra storage might also be possible in the less-than-headroom attic.

765 Square Feet (71.1 Square Meters)

Design

This enticing passive solar home plan has optimized livability within a structure that has a minimal external-surface-to-interior-volume ratio. The interior can comfortably accommodate a couple with room for guests or a child, or two couples living together (some zoning laws constrain this unrelated occupancy). Whether young or old, married or unmarried, this plan has desirable merit. The plan can be flipped over for persons desiring an east-facing patio that avoids late-in-the-day, severe, western solar exposure.

This residence has a low exterior profile that is illustrated as being partially earth-sheltered and is designed for direct garage access if there is one door to the kitchen. It also can be readily designed as a split-level plan with an up-and-down, half flight from the main living area. This additional lower space can be used for more bedrooms, a bath below with stacked plumbing, a recreation room, a hobby room, or storage.

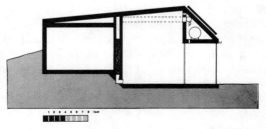

section

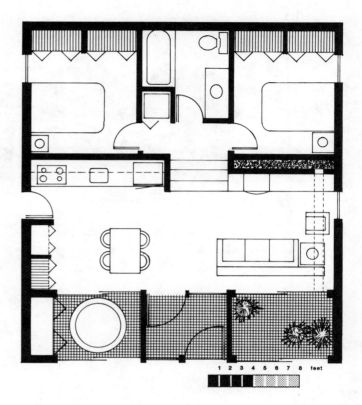

Solar

The south-facing, sectionalized, passive solar sunspaces include the air-locked entry, hot tub sunspace adjacent to the dining and kitchen area, and the sunspace adjacent to the living room area. The thermal mass sunspace floors heat adjacent interior spaces when the inner side-sliding doors are opened.

Solar, direct, and retained gains can subsequently be delivered to a central thermal mass cavity wall filled with gravel by a thermocontrolled, insulated duct and blower system. Slots on the bottom of the mass wall would be provided on the living room side for the return air. Daylighting and secondary solar gains would also serve inner living areas.

Roof-mounted active solar collectors should be sized for both heating domestic hot water and the hot tub. Two covers for the hot tub, one transparent and the other heavily insulated, would help accept and retain passive as well as active solar gains.

Ventilating and Cooling

The outer, double-glazed, screened, side-sliding and louvered door of the sunspace can effectively provide ventilation for the sunspaces and the interior. An exhaust ceiling plenum above the bedrooms can be designed to ventilate both the living and bedroom areas. Casement windows can provide cross ventilation.

Features

The 30-inch (76-centimeters) -deep kitchen-cabinet lineup, full-height pantry and dish storage, storage in the hot-tub space, and generous thermal-buffering closets all add to organized living.

The bathroom is relatively large in size. The stacked washer and dryer could be supplanted by a utility-room connection (with outside access) between the kitchen and a garage or be installed on the lower level of a split-level plan.

16

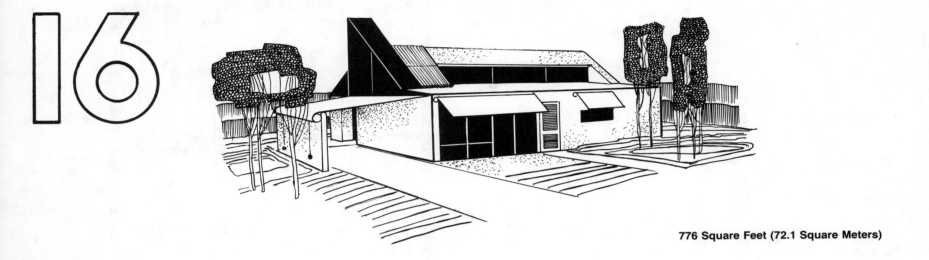

776 Square Feet (72.1 Square Meters)

Design

This rectangular contemporary residence is most suited for a temperate climate. A basement is shown as part of the scheme but could be eliminated in favor of slab-on-grade construction. In such case, the stairway would not be needed and a utility room could take its place. Otherwise, utility functions would be in the basement. The living and dining spaces of this residence are generous in size. Eating in the kitchen is preferred by many people. A small family, a couple, two couples, mingles, or a single who has visiting guests or relatives will find this plan to be appropriate. The open living-dining area would lend itself well to entertaining.

Solar

An extensive clerestory arrangement with vertical, corrugated-metal, solar-radiation-selective-coated interception panels behind single glazing would serve to heat a rear, heavily insulated plenum. A motorized blower preferably operating on photovoltaic cells could deliver this solar-heated air to peripheral rock-bin storage chambers that could have relief slots near the basement floor. This relatively

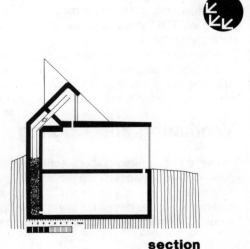

section

102

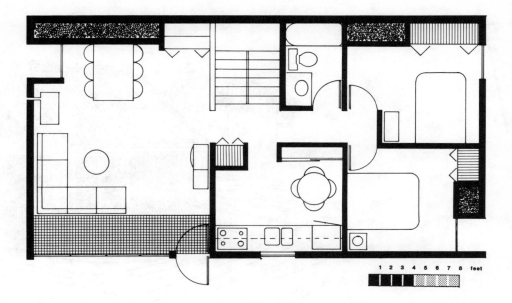

low temperature system would provide radiant energy to interior, non-insulated walls, but with heavily insulated exterior walls. Gravel can be retained by cross supports and heavy-wire mesh. Convection from the solar-heated chambers would pick up south passive solar gains from the living room thermal concourse. Added thermal mass can be provided along the southside glazing of the living room as needed. The principal advantage of this perimeter, mean-temperature method of heating is the balance of temperature that it provides to the interior. Evacuated-tube fluid-type solar collectors are indicated for heating domestic hot water.

Ventilating and Cooling

The roof should be as highly reflective as possible for summertime cooling and to increase solar impact on the clerestory-plenum system in winter. The plenum can also effectively be used in summer to increase interior ventilation in conjunction with a west solar plenum designed with an aspirating slot at the apex to increase the inductive, interior ventilation and cooling when outdoor temperatures are in the cool-to-moderate range. The west plenum of dark sheet metal will perform better with eutectic-salt tubes as a concentrated, phase-change thermal mass to sustain inductive ventilation. Such ventilation will not work for hot-humid areas.

Lateral awnings for south shade and a stretch cover in tension over a west wall will both shade the west elevation of the house and act as a carport. (Where snow occurs, a structural, supportive roof deck under the canvas will be necessary.)

Features

Separation of the bedrooms from the living area can be a benefit when someone wants to sleep while another or others listen to music, watch TV, or converse in the living area. An outside-vented, kerosene-, oil-, or gas-fired supplemental space heater is illustrated for the living and dining area.

848 Square Feet (78.8 Square Meters)

Design

This habitat is designed for a liberated person or a couple who have friends, like to entertain, or may, at times, want to provide sleeping space for an occasional visitor. The architecture is compact, but its interior is free and open. The high ceiling; loft space; circular stairs; open main-level bedroom (with folding door); and large glass areas to the floor create visual space and excitement. A discrete patio wall, fence, or landscaping can add to privacy.

Solar

A direct gain passive solar system with a thermal mass floor is primary to this design. A reflective-roof canopy, oriented to the south, will concentrate solar radiation on an interior black-coated duct that can both destratify interior air at the ceiling apex and place the solar

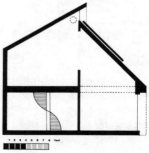

section

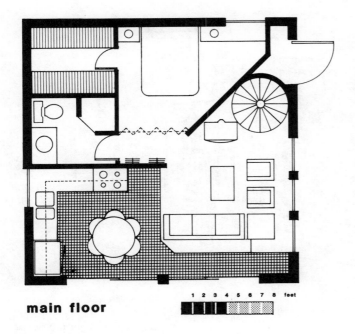

main floor

1 2 3 4 5 6 7 8 feet

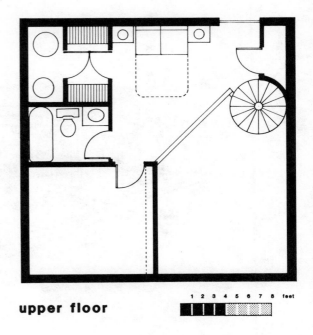

upper floor

1 2 3 4 5 6 7 8 feet

heat gains in a subfloor, gravel plenum or a basement, rock-bin storage (if a basement is provided). The relatively large south roof area leaves adequate space for solar collectors for domestic hot water heating as well as for interior space heating where passive solar access is inadequate.

Ventilating and Cooling

Sliding glass patio doors and operable windows for incoming air and a high ceiling, inductive exhaust can be used for ventilation and seasonal cooling. Evaporative or other forms of mechanical cooling, including heat pumps, can be used. Supplemental heating should be chosen that matches the perceived conditions.

Features

An outside-access garden-and-work-tool closet is provided. The entry is through one of the glass sliding doors. The circular stairway can spiral downward into a basement if such is desired. In these square plans, the roof can be oriented 180 degrees from the plan presented and thermal mass can be provided along the glazed area adjacent to the circular stairs.

18

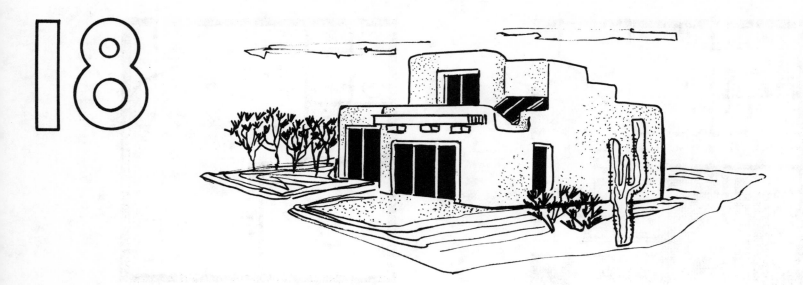

850 Square Feet (79 Square Meters)

Design

For every plan there can be a number of different elevations and designs. To contrast these possibilities, a simple, minimal, wood enclosure or a stucco, monoacrylic coating or adobe design can be developed. In any case, the design should be tailored to the climate and to its site. The almost identical duplication of bedroom facilities with generous living, dining, and kitchen amenities would provide well for two singles, two couples, extended-stay visitors, or children.

Solar

Passive solar direct gain systems with vertical, water-tube thermal storage for the living room with a limited thermal mass floor, as well as a large thermal mass floor area for the dining room provide wintertime radiant heating. Heat rises, requiring a destratification blower and duct to recirculate passive solar and internal heat gains. Roof-mounted solar collectors are shown for domestic hot water heating.

106

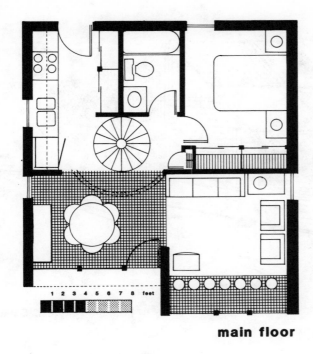

main floor

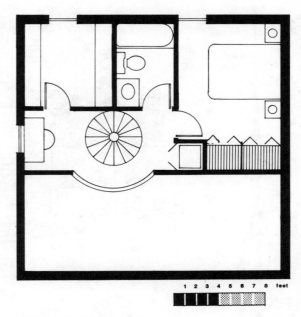

upper floor

Ventilating and Cooling

The high living-area ceiling and two-story interior are compatible with natural ventilation and cooling. There is a tendency for second-floor spaces to overheat. Well-placed doors and windows will aid natural air flows. Supplemental heating can be met by systems previously discussed for other homes of this book.

Features

The spiral stairway saves space. Interior arrangements may allow an expandable-seating dining table. The dining room could seat ten to twelve persons. As with virtually all of the plans presented, the plumbing of the kitchens and baths is integrated. A stacking washer and dryer is indicated on the upper level for easy access. A large storage closet is provided on the second level.

874 Square Feet (81.2 Square Meters)

Design

This compact, affordable home has a romantic ambience. The south-facing lower-level courtyards; roof-top sun deck; and broken roof lines contribute to this feeling. The plan can satisfy the need for two bedrooms and a recreation room; three bedrooms; or a double, two-level unit with single bedrooms, kitchens, and living room space for each. The roof deck primarily serves the upper level. It would be a great spot for viewing an ocean, lake, river, mountain, or other vista.

Solar

To some extent, the solid courtyard railings will shade lower glazed windows. However, direct solar gains received by the thermal slab and the hot spa-pool will provide heat at the lowest level, which will in turn benefit the upper level. Direct solar gains can be captured by thermal-storage bunkers holding eutectic salts. Another option is capturing solar heat gains by means of a heat-absorbing, glass envelope and storing the energy in a central interior rock bin located under the stairway. Evacuated-tube collectors are illustrated on the roof area for use in heating domestic hot water.

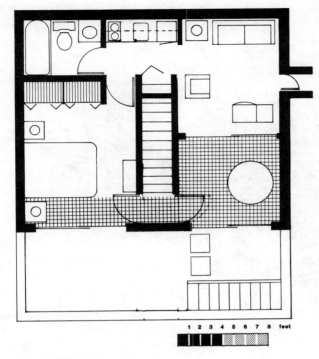

lower floor

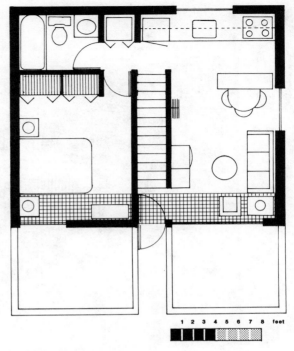

main floor

Ventilating and Cooling

The rectractable roof canopy and awnings can provide summer shade. The lower-level courtyards will have a cool-summer and warm-winter environment, thereby earth-tempering the air as it enters the house. Louvered, awning-type windows; the louvered entry door; and the lower-level, glass sliding doors will provide intake ventilation. A pivoted, ventilating window above the stairway will admit daylight and provide exhaust ventilation. The open-roof deck can benefit from outdoor breezes. The lower level is earth cooled. Supplemental heating is described in the text.

Features

The tent-like canvas over a roof pole will cool down the roof-deck area, and the awnings would provide color. The bridge to the entry provides a defined and pleasant approach.

109

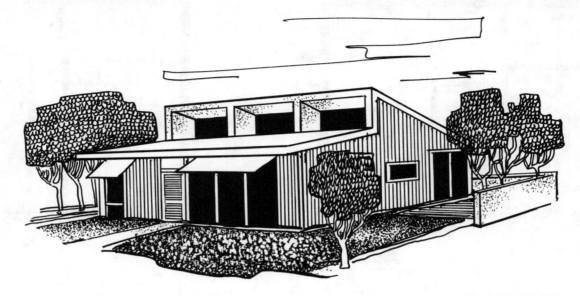

950 Square Feet (88.3 Square Meters)

Design

This home is designed as a one-level three-bedroom or two-bedroom living unit. It can easily accommodate a family with two children. It is a plan with practical and economic space flexibility. The simple exterior design with low lines could fit with zero-property-line zoning or be connected with a common wall as a reverse-plan duplex.

Solar

The clerestory windows with reflective exterior surrounds and reflective roof can use solar radiation to heat eutectic-salt containers. The clerestory glazing could use suspended, high-transmissivity films to reduce reradiant interior losses or have movable insulation. Direct solar gains can heat eutectic salt or water thermal storage as well as the floor (the north wall could also be used) of the dining room that could receive some solar radiation from the east patio door and the clerestory. Interior daylighting of this home would be excellent.

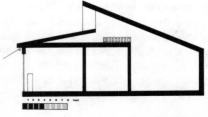

section

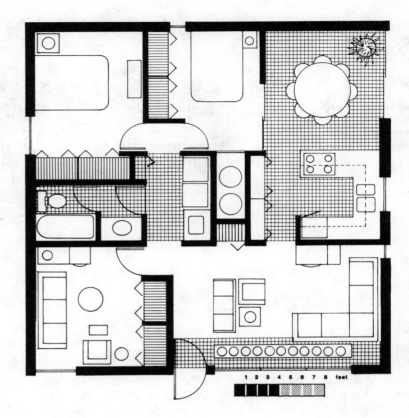

Ventilating and Cooling

Tension-arm awnings, which could roll up under a small overhang, could improve shade as needed. The high ceiling area over the central architectural core is ideal for roof ventilation with controllable dampers. Cross ventilation through all rooms will aid seasonal cooling. Periodic supplemental heat can be used to balance the solar heating.

Features

The centralized energy core has an excellent position to serve all the interior spaces. It also acts as an acoustical buffer for the bedrooms. The dining area can function for numerous alternative uses. The kitchen is well appointed and forms a spacious area with the clerestory-lighted dining room. The bath is divided to increase its functional use by a two-compartment arrangement. An east patio with access to the kitchen and dining areas would be shaded by the house from the west sun.

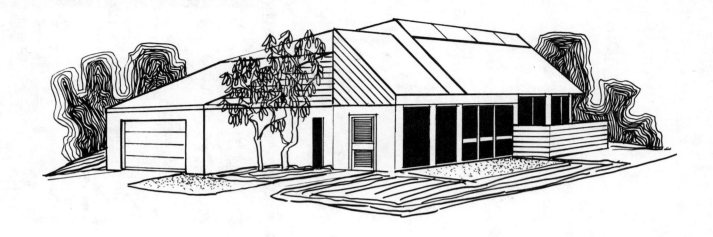

960 Square Feet (89.2 Square Meters)

Design

This single-family home with an attached double-car garage has a luxury flavor but is more costly to build than other designs in this book. Although it has only one bedroom with den (possible second bedroom), the distinctly defined open-plan spaces for kitchen and dining and living rooms give it an airy quality.

The den room is planned as a multi-use space together with the sunspace. This home is for a person who wants to have luxury living within a compact scale. A partially finished basement under the main living area of the house is contemplated and has a stairway at the entry for direct access (ideal for visiting children or family recreation).

Solar

The large south-facing roof area can be used effectively for solar heating of domestic hot water plus partial or more-extensive interior space heating. As such, it would lend itself well to an air-type, active solar collection system.

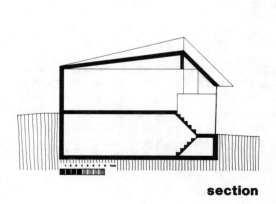

section

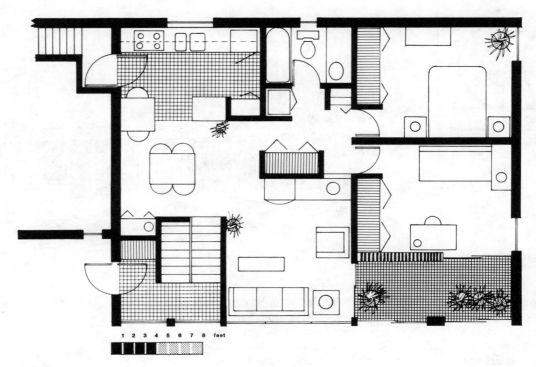

1 2 3 4 5 6 7 8 feet

The main entryway (steps could be included) with a thermal mass and the inner, heavy, thermal mass wall of the sunspace act as supportive passive solar subsystems (more mass can be added to the floor or with free-standing units as advised). A destratification system should use the basement thermal mass as an energy storage system.

Ventilating and Cooling

Cross ventilation as a diagonal function of room spaces is thoughtfully planned. The sunspace can be advantageously vented as a separate element. It is planned to open to an outdoor raised deck or balcony proportioned to avoid shading from a solid railing. The louvered entry door; peripheral, floor-level, awning windows; and patio doors can well supply and control intake air. Exhaust functions can be either inductive or powered. The earth-coupled basement can aid as a cooling reservoir during hot weather and as a thermal-retreat space.

Features

The kitchen is well appointed for gourmet and party cooking. The bath is shielded from the living and dining areas. Stacked washer and dryer are located next to the bath. A dry bar is suggested adjacent to the entry stairway. The den room with a closet is readily convertible to a regular bedroom. The high garage ceiling can accommodate storage. Ample room is provided to seat ten to twelve persons for dining either by joining the separate kitchen and dining tables or using table extensions.

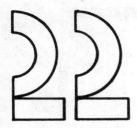

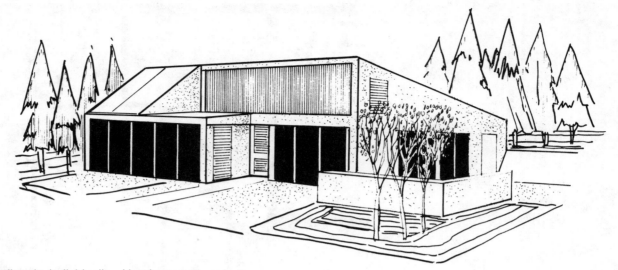

974 Square Feet (90.5 Square Meters)

Design

Every site has its own microclimatic individuality. Herein are a number of passive, hybrid, and active solar design options that are based on the same floor plan. The question is how to originate and develop the most effective and economic life-cycle design solution.

Variations of designs 22 and 23 are presented to demonstrate a few of the solar resolutions that can be accomplished. The two perspective designs, with their appropriate sections, illustrate some of the solar system concepts. The simple two-bedroom plan with two sunspaces and an exterior-accessible storeroom can meet a wide range of individual, mingle, or family needs. The northeast-facing atrium can serve as a lounging space for the master bedroom, as a greenhouse, or as an expansion of the living area for dining or sitting.

Solar

The passive solar subsystems of design 22 are, namely: direct gain with bunker-type thermal storage for the living room; early morning and clerestory gains for the northeast atrium; and direct gain for the large sunspace that also accommodates utility functions. (A clothesline will make this an excellent clothes-drying chamber.) In addition to these solar subsystems, which can have thermal mass in the floor and/or walls, the clerestory or attic solar variations add another element contributing to wintertime heating. This preponder-

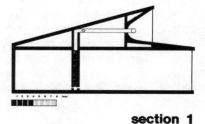

section 1

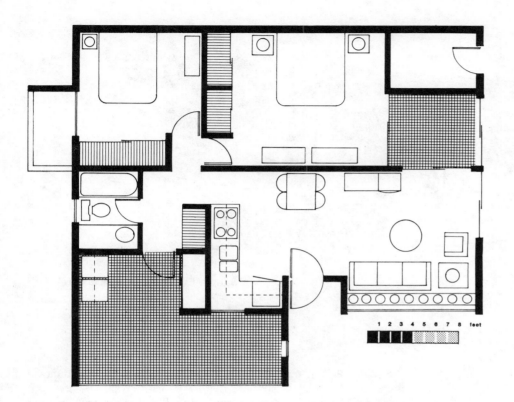

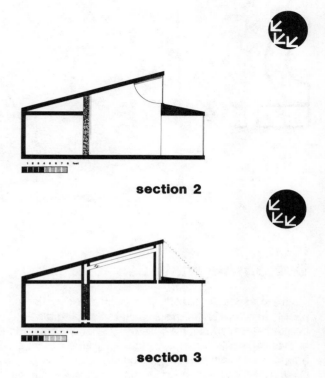

section 2

section 3

ance of solar opportunity can be of particular importance in a cold climate. Relatively low-temperature thermal mass storage that requires less regulatory control is indicated on the sectional drawings. Except for the direct clerestory-solar gain to a centralized thermal mass (with movable insulated panel), the solar clerestory and attic systems require fan power that could be met with photovoltaic cells using a direct-current motor. Domestic hot water can be heated by a fluid-type solar collection system.

Ventilating and Cooling

Cross ventilation through the attic and sunspace with that design can relieve the summertime heat buildup. Side-sliding patio doors; a louvered entry door; and windows can provide intake air for a roof or exhaust stack. An earth berm at the rear would aid cooling. The

large vertical sunspace design with vertical glass will receive less direct sun in summer than the sloping glazed members.

Features

The east patio will be shaded late in the day. An extra sink for convenience could be accommodated in the utility area of the large sunspace. A basement might be provided with a doubleback stairway in place of the northeast exterior-access storage room.

The kitchen can be visually screened from the living room with a vertical grillework or suspended design.

Harold Hay's patented Skytherm North passive solar system that uses water bags over a thermal-conductive ceiling is applicable as another practical option. The system can also provide summer cooling. For concept engineering information, see the reference section.

115

974 Square Feet (90.5 Square Meters)

Design Alternatives

This perspective sketch illustrates a design variation from Compact Home No. 22. In this design the sloping glazing, most likely to be double-walled clear acrylic for cost economy and the practicality of avoiding costly laminated glass, provides a more dynamic exterior appearance. This design solution would be less costly to build than Design No. 22, inasmuch as an active solar system for domestic hot water is eliminated in favor of various solar hot water, direct gain heat exchanges using direct water or air-to-water conversion. Blackened fin tubes can be used for this purpose. Other cost savings can be attributed to the less costly enclosure of the greenhouse utility space, but this comes with a loss of some useful headroom.

Solar System Alternatives

Section 1 illustrates a simple job-built system that uses a large, attic-formed parabolic reflective material such as highly reflective aluminum sheets, coatings, or foil. The parabolic reflector concentrates the sun's rays upon a black-coated, horizontal metal duct about 12 inches (30.5 centimeters) in diameter that using a blower fan will thermally heat vertical gravel retained between two masonry walls. Slots at the bottom would allow for return air in such a manner to also pick up the residual heat from the greenhouse and living room subsystems.

Section 2 is a concept with a wintertime, direct gain, dark-to-medium color solid masonry or thermal concrete wall. The concrete can be stained, painted, or covered with a flat, dark or medium color tile. The lower exterior roof deck would be reflective to increase interior thermal gains. The vertical glazing of double-walled clear acrylic or clear double-glazed glass would have a top-hinged, counterweighted, insulative panel that could be manually or mechanically operated. A more costly sophistication would be with the panel actuated to direct solar gains by a time-lag photoelectric eye device.

Section 3 is either a job-built or manufactured vertically glazed air-type collector (see details from technical manuals on the design and fabrication of air-type collectors). Vertical glazing of low-iron glass and solar radiation absorption plates with selective coatings (that do not outgas to cloud up the collector) would be preferable. A blower fan could heat charge a centralized double thermal mass wall with gravel or store the sun's energy in an insulated rock bin unit in a basement (if such is desired) as in section 4 or under floor in a less controlled storage system like section 5.

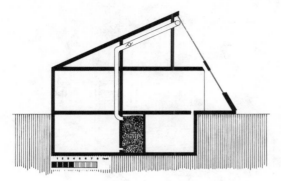

section 4

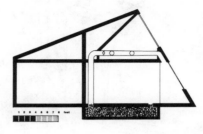

section 5

Section 4 (refer to No. 23) illustrates an attic-type hybrid solar gain system that picks up the residual and sustaining direct passive solar gains from the greenhouse, utility, and living room spaces. A motorized blower fan would heat charge an insulated rock bin that could be controlled to time release its stored solar heat most appropriately to home heating needs. Return air from the rock bin storage could also heat concrete or masonry thermal mass basement walls that are insulated on the outside, as well as pass through floor slots to the greenhouse and living room, through the solar-heated attic that could be covered with black-painted metal lath to convert more solar heat to the air streams, and subsequently back to the rock bin.

Section 5 (refer to No. 23) is an air-type solar system variation of the hybrid attic system shown in section 4. To more effectively capture the prevailing solar radiation, lateral loops of metal ductwork receive both direct solar radiation and that from a specular (highly reflective) surface above the ductwork. The solar loop shown depicts lateral rock bin storage under the main living area (less is needed under bedrooms) that would provide direct radiation to the floor as well as pick up sustaining solar gains from the air and thermal masses provided in the greenhouse and living room areas.

Ventilating and Cooling

The solar systems can be used in warm and hot weather to inductively increase ventilation and interior cooling. In dry climates, stay-dry cooling could be used to charge gravel thermal storage provisions as well as for direct space cooling.

Ventilation louvers with insulated interior hinged doors are shown on both designs 22 and 23 that can be manually activated with pulley chains and cords or motorized with or without a thermo-responsive control. Solar photovoltaic-powered fans would be appropriate for solar attic ventilation and as an aid to cooling in summer.

Features

Design No. 22 provides some material advantages in avoidance of dust, water staining from rain and snow, and leakage over design 23.

Although five variations of passive direct gain and hybrid solar designs are presented, innumerable other alternatives rest only upon the experience and ingenuity of the architect or building designer.

117

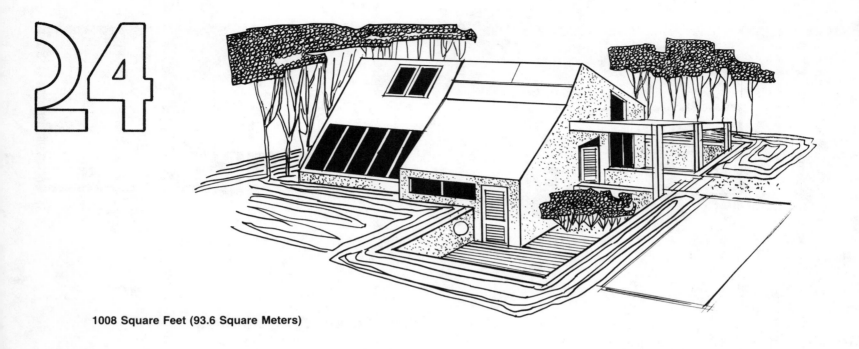

24

1008 Square Feet (93.6 Square Meters)

Design

This earth-coupled habitat emerges from the earth as a form that encloses lower-level living spaces, a large sunspace, an upper-level den or study, a studio room, and a bedroom. The two bathrooms are stacked and the kitchen, with ample dining, opens to an outdoor, roof-covered, sunken courtyard that could also be a pleasurable dining area. It could be screened in and weather protected with clear-plastic or canvas side drops. The living room opens to another, more spacious, southeast court.

The separation of upper and lower bedrooms increases privacy between occupants, who may be children or other adults.

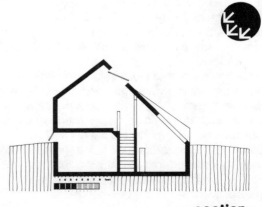

section

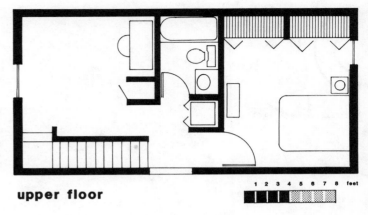

upper floor

1 2 3 4 5 6 7 8 feet

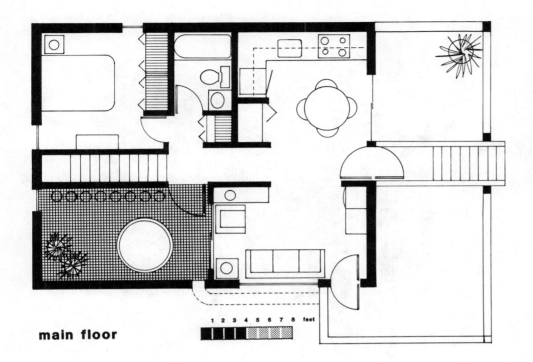

1 2 3 4 5 6 7 8 feet

main floor

Solar

The solar sunspace would most likely be used as a greenhouse. Because of the sloping glass, solar control and movable insulation will be a must for thermal control and containment. Thermal mass water or eutectic-salt tubes can provide the storage mass. A hot tub would be a natural for this space. An inner glazed door would provide daylighting and secondary solar gains to the hall through a glass sliding door to the living room. Operable windows set into the south roof would provide daylight and thermal gains to the upper level. Active solar collectors can not only be used to heat domestic hot water but can be adequate in number to heat the hot tub (which should have an insulative cover). As deemed climatically necessary, the entire south roof can be covered with solar collectors for general space heating.

A destratification system should be utilized to uniformly balance indoor winter temperatures.

Ventilating and Cooling

Louvered exterior doors with solid interior doors control air intake as does the lateral underground duct extending through the west patio wall and terminating for air delivery in the sunspace. Patio sliding doors and operable windows will aid in cross ventilation. Stack-action roof vents can be used to exhaust air.

The subterranean aspect of this home gives it an earth-cooling advantage.

Features

Covering one patio and leaving the other open to the sky can serve various purposes. This house would lend itself well to entertaining both indoors and outdoors.

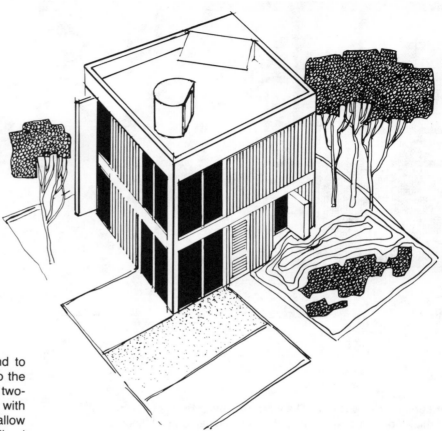

1033 Square Feet (96 Square Meters)

Design

Setting a square-plan home on a site at an angle will tend to make it look larger. A series of these homes set at an angle to the street would moderate their cost-saving, boxy appearance. The two-level sunspaces act as passive solar direct gain systems with thermal mass floors and, with the circular stairway, will allow convected air to rise to the second floor. The roof deck is visualized as being accessible for outdoor living by means of circular-stairway access and pent enclosure.

Solar

The triangular sunspace accepts morning and afternoon as well as midday solar radiation. It also acts as a climatic interlude to the interior. A thermal destratification system can tie into the north, rock-bin, solar-thermal storage. The centralization of heat is a plus value, particularly in a very cold climate. A thermosiphon-concentrator or conventional solar collection system can be provided for domestic hot water.

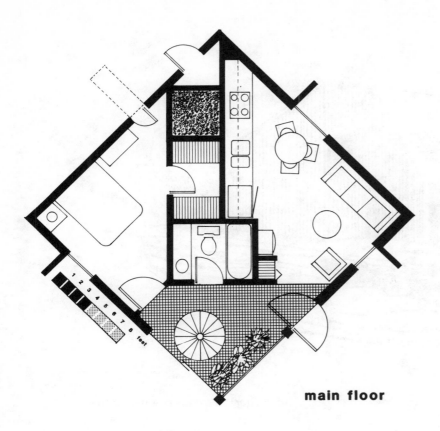

main floor

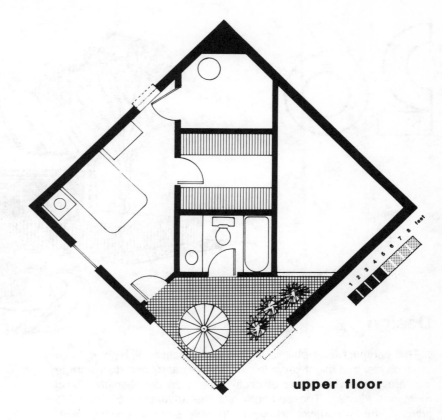

upper floor

Rooftop, air-type solar collectors can be provided to both charge the rock bin with a higher temperature and use an air-to-water heat exchanger for solar heating domestic hot water. Projecting architectural fins aid daylighting.

Ventilating and Cooling

The circular roof pent over the circular stairway would make an ideal high-point ventilation exhaust. Its form would tend to increase inductive air flows. The earth berm can temper lower-bedroom ventilation. The louvered entry, awning windows, and patio doors (railing at upper level) combine for effective ventilation. Supplemental cooling and heating should be appropriate for the climate.

Features

A parapet or railing around the roof deck would provide safety. A view of the living spaces below can occur from the upper sunspace. The energy core includes kitchen, bath, utility room, and solar. Garden-tool storage is accessible to the exterior. Generous storage space is provided.

Design

This compact floor plan is simple and practical. A high, cabinet room divider that might serve the kitchen for pantry and dish storage can provide a visual and physical separation between the living room and kitchen. The bedroom has the advantage of northside privacy. The upper-level loft room can have a conventional double-back stairway instead of the circular one illustrated. A partition and door on the upper level can provide privacy. A bathroom and closet space serves this upper area that, with an operable roof-window installation, can provide required escape and ventilation. The attic storage acts as a northside climatic buffer. The south-facing entry door would not necessarily require an air-locked vestibule.

Solar

The dining area, greenhouse, and entry are planned for direct passive solar gain with thermal mass floor storage. The area and angle of the south-facing roof are well suited to hold active solar collectors for interior-space and domestic water heating. The solar hot water storage can be located in attic space if the floor system is designed to be structurally adequate.

1040 Square Feet (96.6 Square Meters)

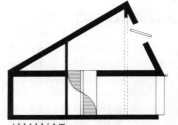

section

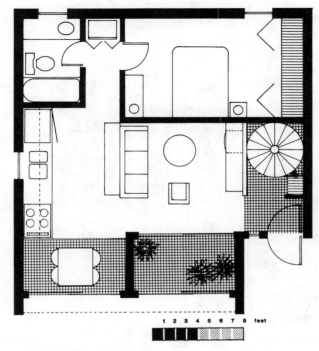

main floor

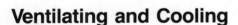

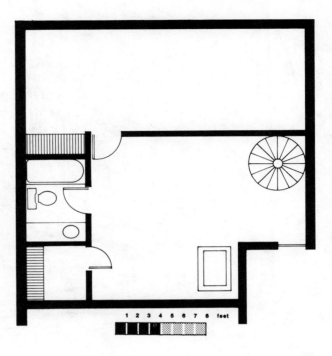

upper floor

Ventilating and Cooling

The high-level upper ceiling can be used for roof stack ventilation and natural cooling. The attic can be designed with a west-facing uninsulated exterior surface and insulated interior to increase inductive ventilation in such climates where it is appropriate. Air intake can be accomplished by the side-sliding, screened doors of the dining room; greenhouse; and sunscreened, louvered entry door. Lower awning sash members of the windows can serve for screened ventilation and cooling.

Features

On the east wall between the main entry and the stairway, pegs can be used for coat hanging. A divider between the circular stairway and living room can be of any height or be glass, or the entire entry can be air-locked. The main-entry door can open east instead of south and the greenhouse can be extended the full width of the house. In good weather, the dining table can be moved to the south patio through the sliding door for outdoor dining. The bath is accessible to the bedroom as well as to the living area. A stacking washer and dryer are located in that hall.

Design

This energy-conserving design has a practical sunspace with hot-spa pool and an abundance of closet and storage space. Access to an attached garage can be through the main floor storeroom. This dwelling can encompass many different life-styles. The proximity of the stairway to the single entry door reduces traffic through the main floor living area. The square architectural plan can be oriented south from any direction of street access.

Solar

The direct gain sunspace with floor, hot tub, and stairway provide thermal mass. The thermal mass floor that extends into the living area will also retain direct solar winter gains, with the sunspace acting as a thermal barrier. The thermal mass wall between the sunspace and living room and the west wall (insulated on the exterior) can materially improve passive solar performance. Roof-mounted solar collectors with a thermal tank in the upper storage space can heat the domestic hot water and spa tub.

1058 Square Feet (98.3 Square Meters)

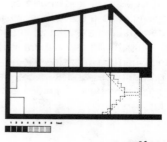

section

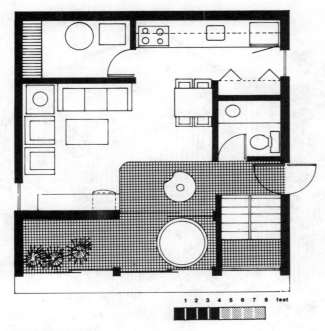

main floor

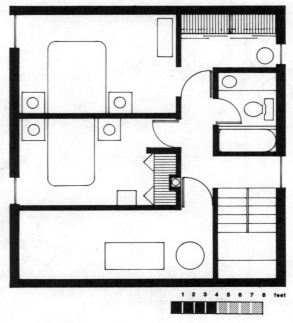

upper floor

Ventilating and Cooling

The sliding doors of the sunspace, the louvered entry door, and the operable windows of the kitchen, living room, bedrooms, and dressing area can provide cross ventilation and function with roof ventilation at the ridge line. The roof overhang (determined by climate and latitude) can provide welcome summer shading. Second-floor bedrooms present greater hot-weather cooling problems than main-level space. Supplemental units can provide periodic space heating.

Features

The lower-level storage can easily be plumbed for a darkroom. The hot-spa pool is optional. The space-heating stove in line with the entry is also optional. The hot water tank with a solar preheat tank and the washer-dryer combination can connect to the plumbing line from the adjoining kitchen. Bathroom plumbing is stacked.

125

28

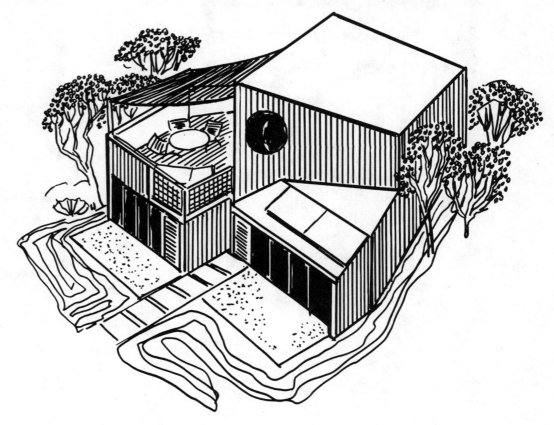

1080 Square Feet (100.3 Square Meters)

Design

This ingriguing, triangular-plan habitat with an upper studio room offers an open upper-level deck that could be shaded with a suspended sunscreen. The open deck, combined with the upstairs room, would serve well for indoor-outdoor entertainment and gatherings. The upper studio room might particularly appeal to the researcher, writer, artist, or musician as a workshop or home office. The lower plan is organized to separate the kitchen and dining room from the living-room area.

Solar

The very large sunspace and the direct gain passive solar dining-kitchen area will provide an extensive heating system. Thermal mass floors are simple and logical. As desired, more thermal mass can be added to the sunspace. The living room is well protected by this thermal buffer but will benefit by secondary, direct solar radiation in winter. Movable insulation is illustrated. Roof space is provided for solar collectors for heating domestic hot water.

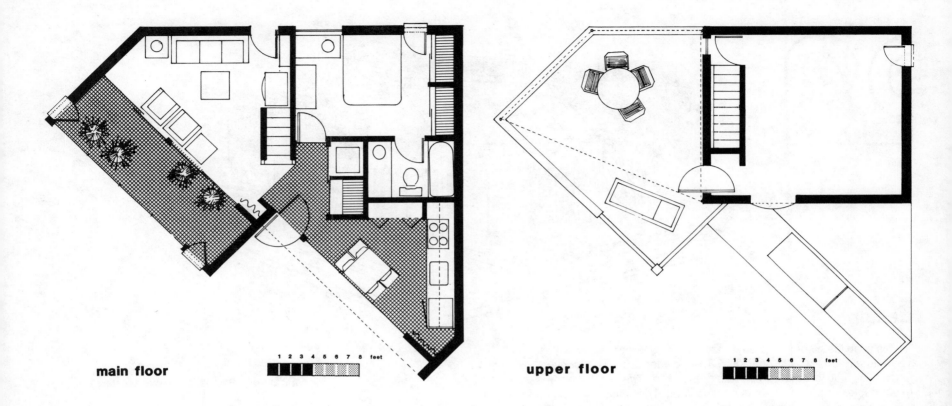

main floor

1 2 3 4 5 6 7 8 feet

upper floor

1 2 3 4 5 6 7 8 feet

Ventilating and Cooling

Ventilation can be easily and effectively provided at the high point of the studio ceiling. All room spaces are designed for cross ventilation aided by the stack action of the stairway. A through-the-wall ventilator for air intake should be located at the far end of the kitchen. The projecting sunspace will provide afternoon shading and, thus, cooling of the dining-kitchen area.

Features

The very large sunspace can challenge an indoor-outdoor gardener or serve a multitude of functions. The triangular plan can be readily earth-sheltered and, by its form, divert cold northerly winter winds. The stacked utility washer and dryer join the bath. The large plastic bubble to the south adds a bit of class. The bedroom is north, away from the solar heat.

29

Design

This is an ideal compact home that effectively separates activities. The kitchen is relatively spacious. The powder room is a convenience. The utility room is separately enclosed. The dining room is expandable. The living room is commodious. The living-room closet can handle a game table, extra chairs, luggage, etc. Closets and storage for the two bedrooms and a separate storage room are unusually large.

A couple at any age or a small family would find this home to be a delight in practicality, ease of maintenance, thermal comfort, daylighting, dimension of space, and gracious entertaining.

Solar

A relatively small sunspace is provided with a thermal mass floor and vertical blinds that are black (or very dark) on one side for conversion of solar radiation to the heating of air and highly reflective on the other. The blinds can also be used to control privacy. The solar heat from the sunspace will migrate upward and be captured along with clerestory solar gains. A lateral, open-ended, black duct can deliver with a motorized fan the solar- and interior-heated (by lights, appliances, and people) air into the centralized rock-bin

1100 Square Feet (102.2 Square Meters)

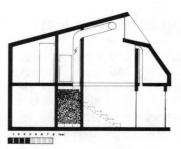

section

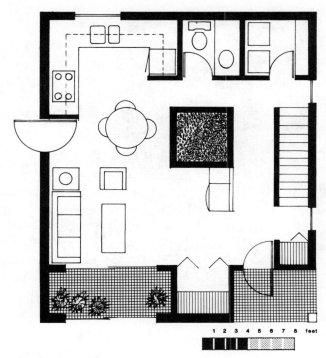

main floor

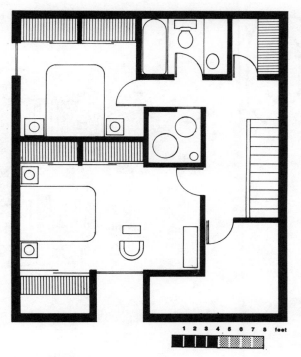

upper floor

storage. Heat loss from preheat-solar and supplemental domestic hot water tanks can be an energy bonus. Active solar collectors are shown for domestic water heating, but adequate sloping-roof space is available for more collection surface, which could be used for partial space heating.

As an option, the clerestory windows could be eliminated and the total south-roof surface be devoted to an active solar air-type system, using the rock bin for centralized thermal storage. A heat exchanger interposed between the collectors and the rock-bin storage can serve the heating of domestic hot water.

Ventilating and Cooling

The south main-entry ventilating door will be shaded in summer and act as a cross-ventilating air intake with a matching, outer

ventilation door to the west as well as operable windows on the lower and upper levels. Inner, fully insulated doors would act to control the inception of outdoor air. The reverse-side reflectivity of the vertical blinds of the sunspace can be used to reradiate the sun's energy outward, thereby reducing the cooling load for the interior. Small overhangs will shade the clerestory and sunspace glazing. Cool nocturnal air can be used to cool the rock bin during warm and hot weather for daytime cooling when indoor temperatures rise.

Features

For all of its functional capabilities, this home requires a minimal site space. A garage can be readily accessed to the east, west, or north. The plan lends itself well to diverse furniture arrangements.

Design

This living unit has an urban appearance and can be effectively aligned as a series of connected townhomes. It can be a real family home with its three bedrooms; conveniently serve visiting guests; provide two upper-level offices for a work-at-home couple; or, house live-in friends. The generous kitchen, dining, and living spaces can handle cooking, eating, and entertainment with style. Garages between units can be easily attached and provided with an entry.

Solar

A bank of eutectic-salt bunkers can be lined up on the south side of the living room. Inner, sliding (or otherwise applicable) doors can provide a solar envelope. The outer glazing would be clear, the inner glazing heat-absorbing; or, dark vertical blinds between the inner and outer glazings could transform solar radiation to airborne heat. This thermal energy could be transported to a subfloor, gravel storage plenum by a fan-assisted hybrid system. Roof-mounted solar collectors and an attic tank can heat and store domestic hot water.

1170 Square Feet (108.7 Square Meters)

section

130

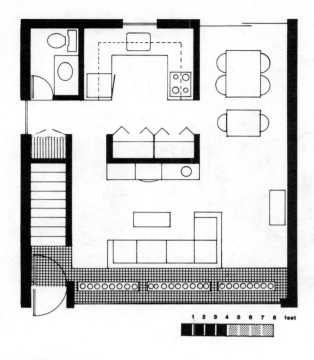

main floor

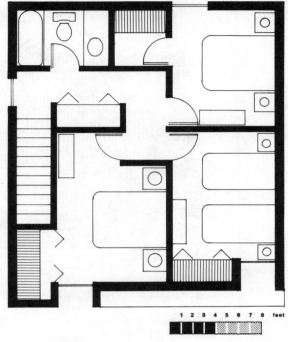

upper floor

Ventilating and Cooling

The projecting upper floor will shade lower windows fully during summer and partly during spring and fall. The screened entry door; the side-sliding, dining-room patio door; and the second floor windows and northside, roof-plenum ventilators will cross ventilate the interior. This plan would lend itself well to pressurized, filtered, nocturnal-air cooling (when nights are cooler) by using the building envelope to obtain outside air. Recessed bedroom windows will provide summer shading.

Features

For economy, the three bedrooms share one bath. The kitchen is out of sight from the living room. The dining space is expandable into the living room. The large living and dining spaces contribute to successful entertaining.

Design

The perspective shows a northern, street-side view of the home with a solar array facing the backyard. The main air-locked entry is shielded from cold north winds but is good access for people alighting from a car. The north-facing garage door could freeze in place — a problem in some climates; thus, where site conditions allow, an east-facing door for a double garage is advised. The roof deck over the garage will receive south sun but be in shade from the west sun for summertime gatherings. A minimal Heat Mirror (interior heat reflective) triple-glazed window is provided for the stairway. A notable advantage of a north-street frontage is that the rear yard can have privacy and south sun.

Solar

The southside elevation, because of the depths of most rear yards, enhances the opportunity for unobstructed passive solar design. Several passive solar subsystems are indicated on the plan. The southside sunspace glazing allows direct solar gain into a thermal mass floor plus water-tube thermal storage. The living room can benefit by a eutectic-salt bunker that leaves most of the full south glazing open to view. The garage is illustrated with solar gain

1200 Square Feet (111.5 Square Meters)

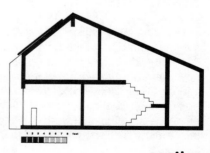

section

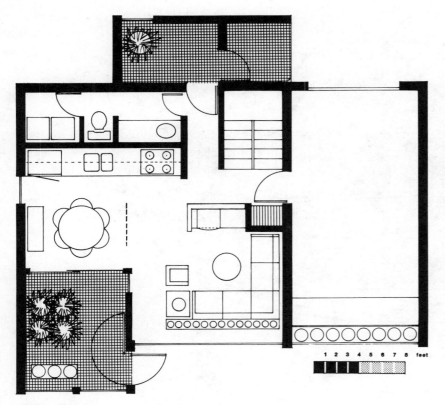

main floor

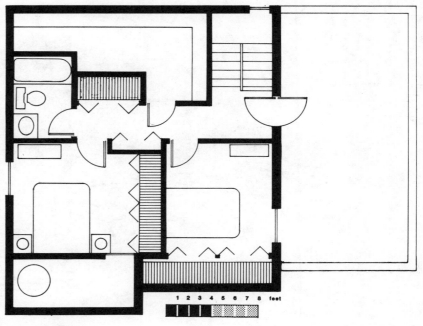

upper floor

water-tube storage that can either serve the garage or, with an inner and an outer glazing material, become a hybrid system to serve the lower living area or upper bedroom. The rear roof angle can be pitched to accommodate active solar collectors to heat either domestic hot water and a hot spa-tub located in the greenhouse (if desired) or for additional space heating.

Ventilating and Cooling

The two-story, high-ceilinged, upper level is ideally suited to inductive ventilation at the apex of the roof. The high upper-level ceiling; open deck to the east for air; and ventilation will aid the cooling process. The west-facing bedroom and dining-area windows should have reflective glass or an external blind to reduce or eliminate the impact of the sun. Outer, louvered, ventilating screen doors for the greenhouse, main entry, and upper-level patio deck will be effective for seasonal cooling and ventilating. Powered-intake ventilation and cooling should be filtered if used.

Features

The main-level powder and utility rooms act as a northside thermal buffer. The large eastside garage acts as an effective thermal buffer. The garage is deep enough to accommodate a home workshop, or a small den could be provided with access from the living room. A hanging-fabric room divider or vertical grillework to separate the dining from the living area and help screen the kitchen is indicated. An open coat closet (or with doors) is provided to serve both the main and garage entries.

32

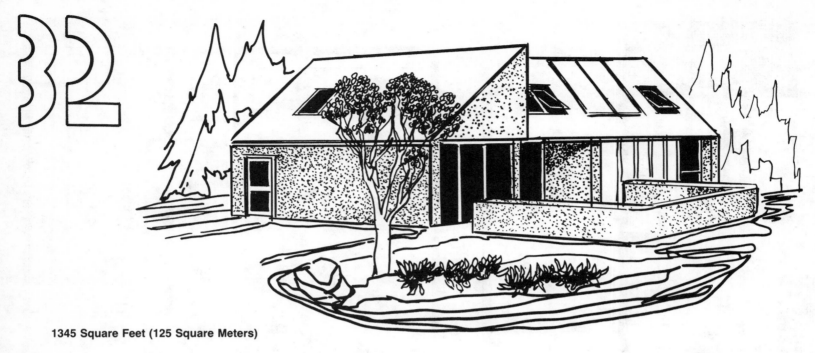

1345 Square Feet (125 Square Meters)

Design

This design is more spacious and well suited for entertaining both indoors and outdoors. The larger kitchen and dining spaces can handle the crowd. The bath is near the bedroom but separately accessible from the living area. Where codes do not permit, a double-back, conventional stairway can be provided for the second-floor level. This is an ideal home for two couples or singles who want to share the same kitchen — although a separate compact kitchen could be provided for the upper level. The plumbing is stacked and each bedroom can enjoy its own privacy and bath. The sunspace and south-facing covered patio offer interseasonal, multiple use.

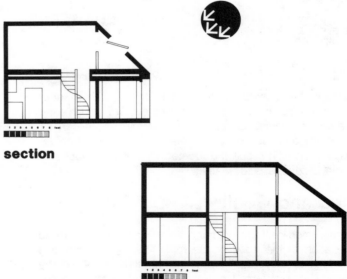

section

section

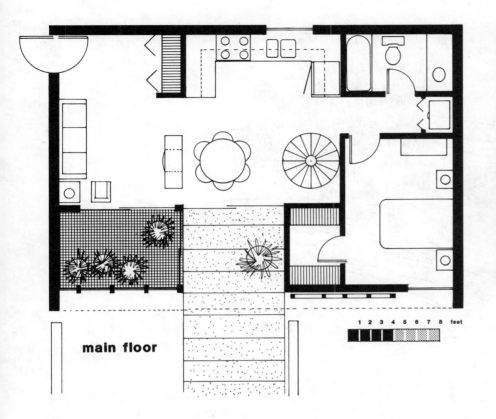

main floor

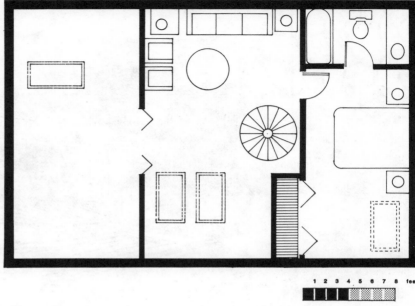

upper floor

Solar

The direct gain passive solar sunspace and a side-sliding, clear-plastic-glazed door form direct gain passive solar chambers that also act as climatic buffers. The south patio can be made into an effective outdoor-living space.

Flat-plate solar collectors on the south roof can take care of domestic hot water and a hot tub if so desired.

Ventilating and Cooling

Flow-through ventilation through the sliding doors of the sunspace and covered-patio area as well as from the ventilation panel entry door and windows should be exhausted at the high point of the roof.

Supplemental heating should be energy efficient and zoned specifically for each level.

Features

The spacious attic can be converted to a studio space, additional sleeping space, or storage. An indoor hot tub in the sunspace or the outdoor covered-patio area with the glazed enclosure door can be heated by use of added solar collection panels.

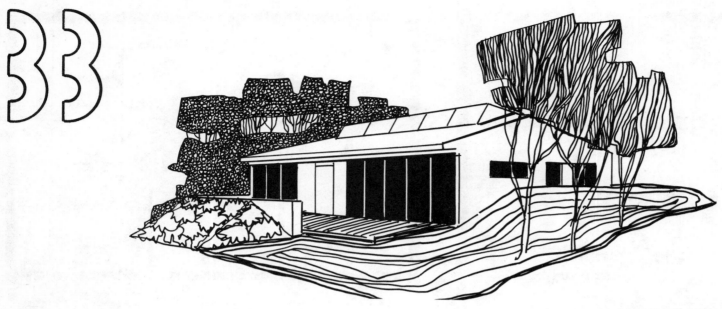

33

1443 Square Feet (134.1 Square Meters)

Design

This midsized one-story home is relatively compact for a very large family. It was contractor constructed in 1981 in Denver at a cost of under $36 per square foot including an active solar system and site improvements. The family of ten find it a delightful, minimal-energy-demand home. It is a home that can provide various dimensions of use. The large dormitory-type room can be divided into two bedrooms or a bedroom and a recreation room or even a lap swimming lane.

Solar

The entire activity space is a direct gain solar system. The dark tile over concrete floor and wainscot provide thermal storage. The greenhouse accepts both primary and secondary direct solar gains. The active solar system is for heating the extensive domestic hot water use. A recirculative blower destratifies the upper levels of solar and internal thermal gains. The greenhouse can be readily enlarged as might be desired.

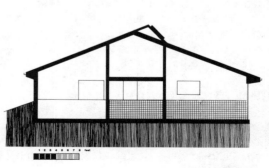

section

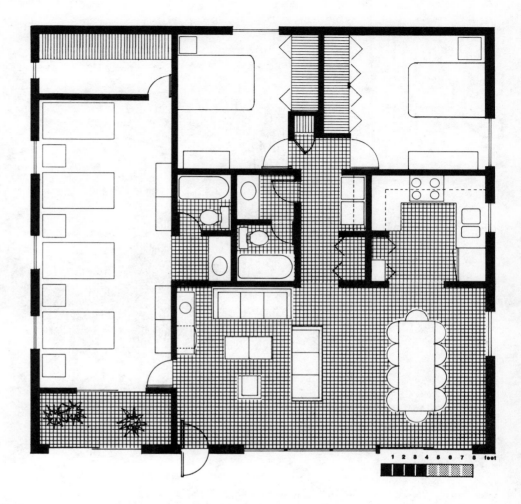

Features

The centralized energy core of kitchen, baths, and utility functions concentrates the internal energies of the home. The space above this energy core provides generous storage and mechanical facility. The home is bermed on three sides for frost-free footings under a concrete slab floor to accomplish earth-coupling for warm weather cooling and to act as a thermal earth barrier.

Earth berms at the south front around a concrete patio wall give privacy and thermal protection. This home performs admirably well through all seasons.

Ventilation

This home is easily cross ventilated by the placement of operable windows. High ribbon windows in the dormitory room minimize westside summer solar gains but optimize ventilation. It is cool in summer without air-conditioning.

137

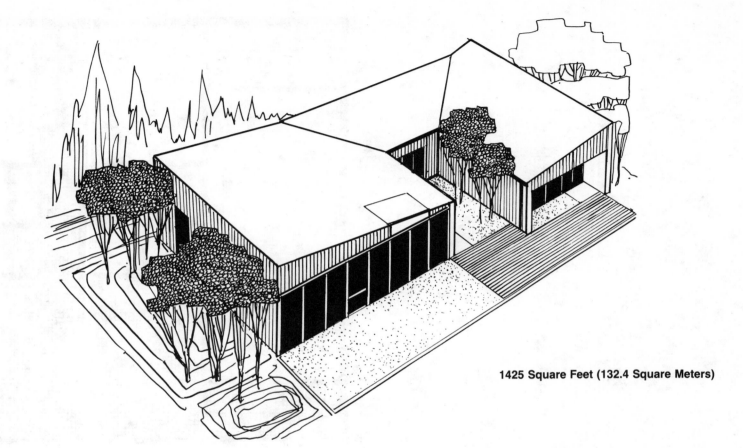

34

1425 Square Feet (132.4 Square Meters)

Design

A forerunner of this compact duplex was designed and constructed by the author in 1952. It was a delightful, energy-conserving home to live in and the smaller living unit of this double provided income and security. The outdoor courtyard was well used as a welcome solar space. Two couples can comfortably and privately live in this abode. A connecting utility room can be used as a guest sleeping space for either unit. The smaller front bedroom can be used as a den. The interior and exterior patio spaces work well for entertainment. The larger unit is a practical, easy-to-maintain home for any age. The rear unit is a good hideaway for a couple or a single.

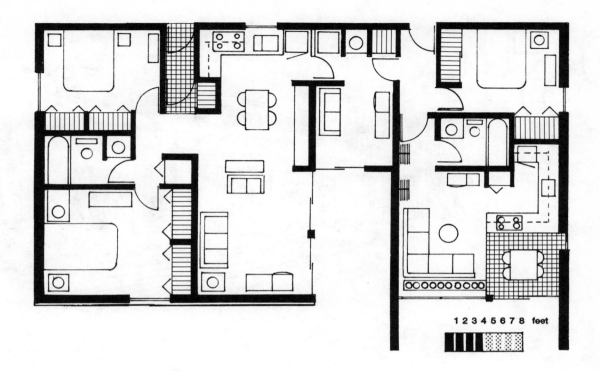

1 2 3 4 5 6 7 8 feet

Solar

The solar courtyard and patio with white marble reflective chips bring ample daylight into the interiors. Roofs that slope toward the courtyard optimize solar access. A glazed trombe wall (vented or unvented) with passive solar gains for the larger unit and thermal mass floor and interior mass walls for the smaller unit serve the living spaces. Trough-type, reflective solar collectors can be roof mounted for heating domestic hot water. The low interior-ceiling height (7 to 8 feet [2.1 to 2.4 meters]) does not justify destratification. A flat skylight at the south edge of the roof of the larger unit provides in-depth interior daylighting.

Ventilating and Cooling

With numerous patio-door openings to the central courtyard and side-sliding, ventilative windows planned for cross ventilation, this house, with its surround of trees, was relatively cool in summer. The low ceiling height was not conducive to inductive ventilation.

Features

West and northside windows are minimized. This home cost little to build. The plan layout allows for an effective arrangement in which the smaller unit can be used for additional space for a larger family; as a home office; or as an arts, crafts, or music studio. This home can be placed on a narrow site when the main street lies either to the west or east.

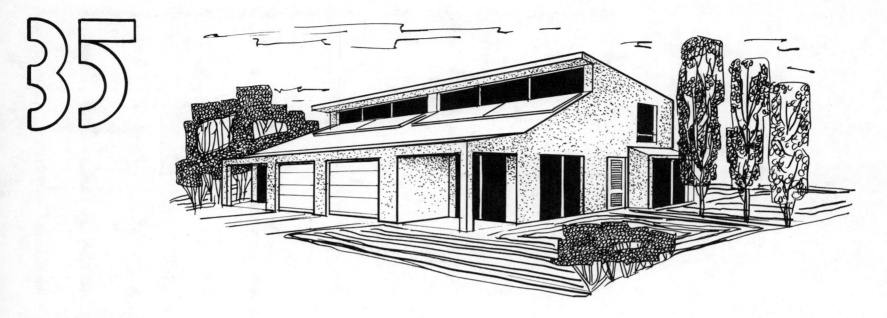

35

Design

This is a real, garage-oriented duplex for individuals for whom the car is as important as the home. They will be forever grateful for this plan, designed with vehicles in mind. There is nothing like a well-kept, vintage Mercedes garaged in a lower-cost compact home.

With compact livability, these duplex units have an option of an outdoor, covered, south-facing patio or enclosed sunspaces. Thus, a desire for either outdoor or indoor living can be well satisfied. The two-level interior space is compact but pleasant and livable. The busy single couple (young or old) will find this bright, daylighted home to be cheerful, energy efficient, and secure. Duplexes tend to provide more security than single or larger multiple living units, as a relationship of concern is more likely to occur.

Solar

The centralized-clerestory passive solar system with masonry or concrete thermal mass wall in addition to wintertime morning gains of the main-level living area of the east unit and afternoon gains of

1110 Square Feet (each unit) (103 Square Meters)

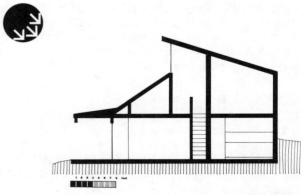

section

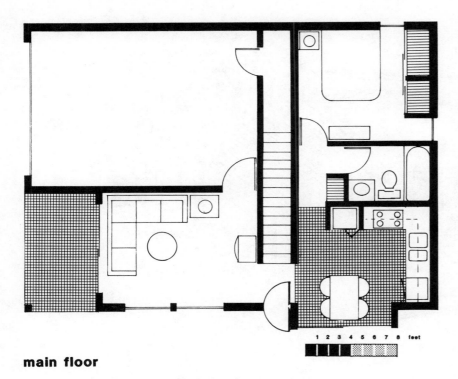

main floor

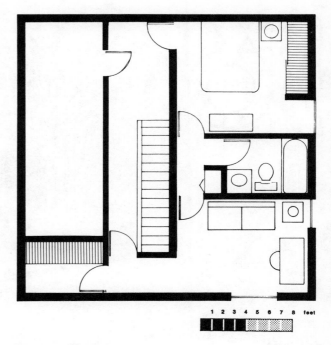

upper floor

the west unit will provide mean radiant thermal comfort. The indicated flat-plate collectors will provide heating for domestic hot water but the south, sloping roof area is large enough — combined with the passive solar systems — to provide 90 to 100 percent of the heating needs for a temperate or cold climate (depending upon winter available insolation). A destratification system is a must for this interior layout and such energy could be stored in a direct-radiant, low-temperature gravel plenum under the living room floor.

Ventilating and Cooling

The central position of the stairway with its high ceiling offers an ideal stack-action condition for peak-of-the-roof ventilation and inductive, interior cooling. The destratification fan can also be de-

signed to mechanically exhaust interior air. Seasonal shading is provided by the clerestory overhang and the covered front patio.

Features

The lower reflective roof deck will increase solar collection and clerestory daylighting. The east and westside entries are protected from the north winter wind by the projecting window bays. Sliding doors from the living and dining nook areas can extend the home for outdoor use. The closet at the main-floor bath can be used for coats, or pegs can be put along the south, upper gallery wall. A huge upper-level storage closet is provided.

36

Design

These relatively large duplex or townhome, attached multiliving units with three bedrooms and den can handle a high family density of home owners (or renters). These dwellings are simple and direct in design and construction. The more the number of individual-dwelling units that are joined, the more energy efficient they become as energy losses are reduced. Land-use density also has the effect of reducing budget costs.

Solar

The passive solar system combines two kinds of thermal mass: water tubes and floor. A thermal destratification system is a must to help redistribute the warmer second-floor ceiling air to the lower level, thereby equalizing the interior comfort of each dwelling. The clerestory windows will accept wintertime, direct solar radiation, but the upper roof overhang will provide shade in summer. A reversing destratification motor can be employed to provide powered summertime ventilation. Domestic hot water is solar heated.

1416 Square Feet (each unit) (131.5 Square Meters)

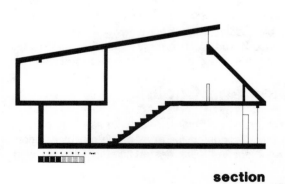

section

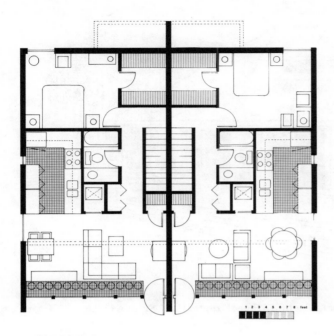

main floor

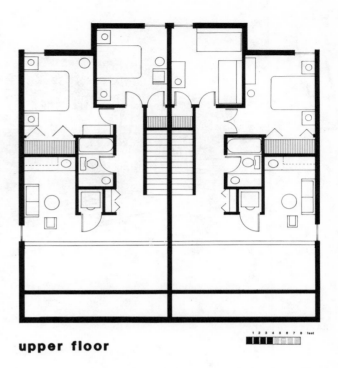

upper floor

Ventilating and Cooling

A principal concern can be for cooling of second-floor spaces because heat rises. Optimizing the use of temperate outdoor air prevailing in each specific microclimate should be a primary step. Natural cross ventilation; stack-effect induction; or, electric — or better yet — photovoltaic-powered heat pumps or air-conditioning are subsequent choices.

Features

The interior volume is relatively large in relation to the outer building envelope. Generous closet spaces are provided. The regularity of the architectural, sectional form makes it easy to join these units as zero-property-line or attached dwellings.

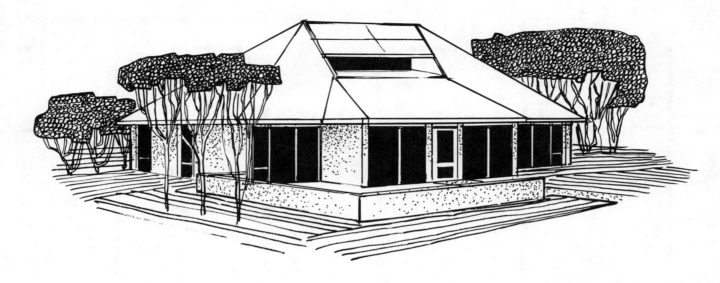

37

1149 Square Feet (574.5 each unit) (106.7 Square Meters [53.4 each unit])

Design

This duplex dwelling with a traditional form has a spacious upper-level loft space that can have a great number of uses. The simple floor plan arrangement separates the dining space for a sense of elegant dining within a relatively compact home. The bath and bedrooms are particularly generous in size. The separation between living room and kitchen is clearly defined. People who like to live the better life and love to entertain will find life comfortable in the interior environment.

Solar

A solar concourse the full width of this dwelling, plus the direct gain dining area and solar-thermal bunkers, receive direct gain passive solar energy. The horizontal regressed window of the loft space with reflective side returns will help illuminate the interior. Solar collectors at the roof peak are for the heating of domestic hot water.

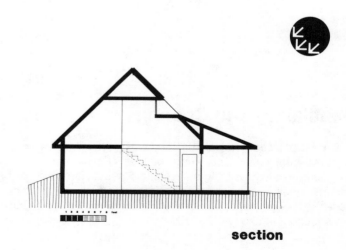

section

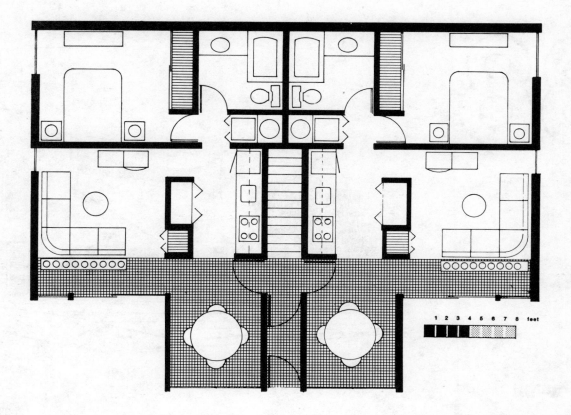

Ventilating and Cooling

In a warmer climate, the large hat-like roof can be extended outward with deeper overhangs, which can provide more shading. Side-sliding doors and low-awning windows are positioned for cross ventilation. The high roof line encourages natural ventilation.

Features

The loft space can be used by either living unit or used under a joint arrangement. The conservative architectural appearance will fit in any conventional old or new neighborhood. Attached garages could be added at either end of the building structure.

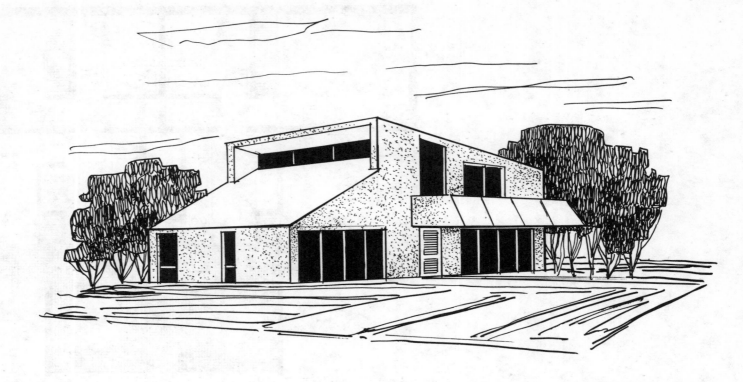

Design

This versatile multidwelling can be three separate living units: two living units with common recreational and guest facilities on the upper level (not illustrated); a single, larger living unit for a family with two or three upstairs bedrooms combined with a lower unit; or, a single residence with five bedrooms and a main-floor division between living, dining, recreation, and a single kitchen.

Thus, three singles, couples, or a family of any reasonable size can be accommodated.

Solar

A south solar concourse runs the full length of this habitat. The thermal mass floor can be augmented by water or eutectic thermal-energy bunkers. The west, deep-set clerestory is principally for daylighting. The vertical stairway glazing will receive passive solar direct gain as well as the lower solar concourse. The accumulated

980 Square Feet (main level) (91 Square Meters)

490 Square Feet (upper level) (45.5 Square Meters)

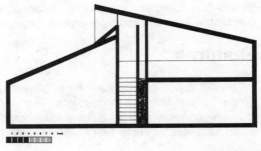

section

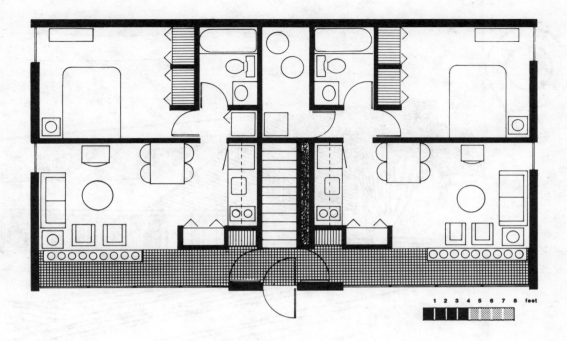

1 2 3 4 5 6 7 8 feet

solar heat will rise and be forced downward through a vertical, centralized gravel plenum with either masonry on each side or retained with a small steel mesh between wood studs. This low-temperature energy will provide a core of winter heat.

Ventilating and Cooling

The upper balcony to the south will act as a shading element in summer. An awning or external blinds can be applied to the west-unit living area's south and west windows. The louvered door as well as peripheral floor-level awning windows and a reversing fan (used for winter heating of the vertical plenum) with a roof stack can exhaust interior air. The upstairs interior space will have the greater need for summer cooling, so heat pumps or conventional air-conditioning may be advised.

Features

In proportion to its number of occupants, this multidwelling will be especially energy efficient. Garages can be readily attached to the lower living units, but this is not easily accomplished with the upper living units. The scale of this three-unit habitat avoids overscaling in comparison to six or more units often combined into one building envelope by developers.

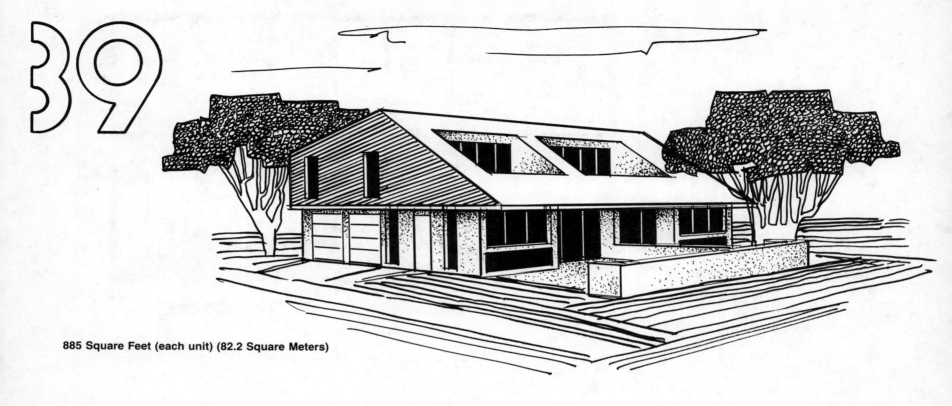

885 Square Feet (each unit) (82.2 Square Meters)

Design

This four-unit home complex, integrated with four single-car garages, will effectively conserve energy. Access is from a protected north entry to the upper levels and the garages. The lower-level units can have either east and west or south main entries. Lower-level units have direct access to garages. These four, two-bedroom units have high ceilings in the living room areas. Acoustical separation between common walls and floors of the living units will be a must. These multiple housing designs offer an investment opportunity for someone who would like to own and manage an energy-efficient project.

1 2 3 4 5 6 7 8 feet

section

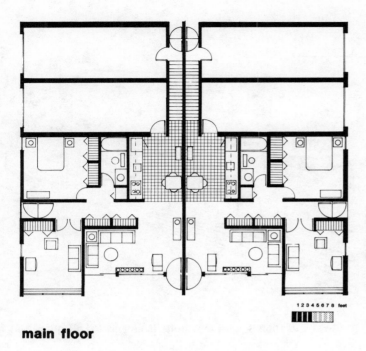

main floor

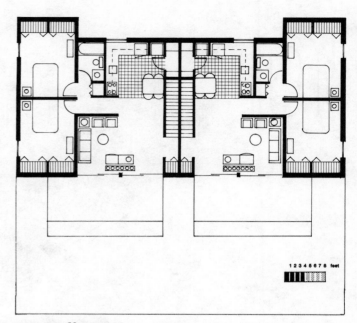

upper floor

Solar

The south-facing upper-patio decks and lower patios to the south benefit by direct solar exposure. Direct gain, lower, thermal mass storage partial walls are visualized for passive solar direct gain with heating to the interior primarily by thermal-lag, water-tube, or eutectic-salt solar-thermal storage bunkers as illustrated design elements located at the glazed areas of the living rooms. Active solar collectors for domestic hot water can be installed across the upper ridge or along the lower south portion of the roof.

Ventilating and Cooling

The glass sliding doors to the south will provide direct ventilation. Cross ventilation is available by opening windows to the east and west in phase with the patio-door ventilation. Reverse-cycle heat pumps that also provide cooling, conventional air-conditioning, or evaporative cooling as appropriate for the climate and conditions can be applied.

Features

This foursome offers a high-density concentration with minimal land coverage. The garages incorporated into the building structure act as climatic buffers. Multiple living units incorporated into one structure reduce energy loss and lend a savings in construction cost.

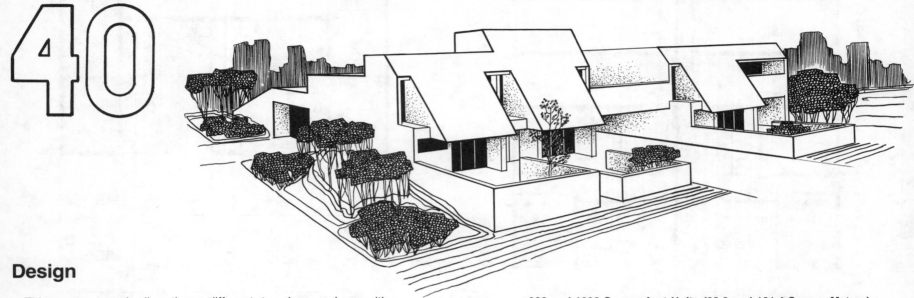

40

Design

This concept embodies three different townhome plans with garages integrated into the overall design. Roof terraces accessible from the second floor are located over intervening garages (or carports) and also to the upper-level rear with exterior walls for territorial definition and privacy and energy-conscious landscaping. The assembled project will make a cohesive design statement but still posses variety. Each compact plan is based on using manufactured energy-core modules that are stacked to centralize plumbing, mechanical, and electrical facilities (note crosshatched areas). Energy core modules are further explained in Appendix H.

Solar

The rear as well as intervening terraces are designed to have solar exposure during the winter months. Sloping roofs to the south offer an opportunity for relatively large areas for flat-plate or photovoltaic solar collection that can be respectively used for domestic hot water, interior space heating, or power supply. The designs are planned for south orientation to the sun with a provision for main-floor enclosed sunspaces or for partial, roof-covered south patios. Upper-level south windows are recessed to avoid the intrusion of the summer sun but to admit direct, wintertime, solar radiation. In

903 and 1092 Square-foot Units (83.9 and 101.4 Square Meters)

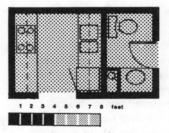 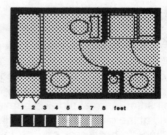

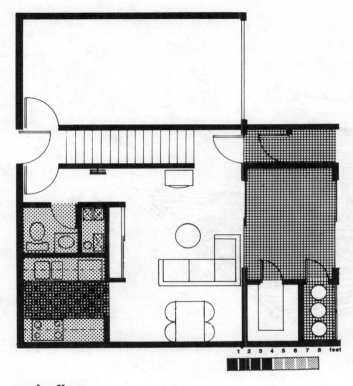

main floor

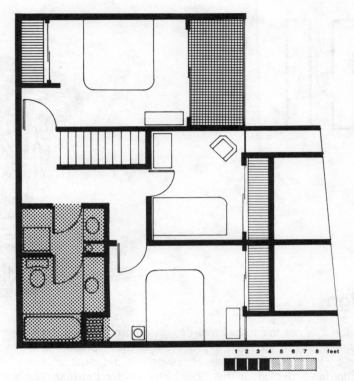

upper floor

any case, roof-located flat-plate solar collectors are advised for domestic hot water heating. A centralized energy-core, thermal-storage module would reside in a basement, matching in overall size the basic core modules. Energy from active, hybrid, and destratification systems as well as from all internal heat from appliances, equipment, lighting, and people would be additive to the centralized thermal storage. Off-peak electric-heat storage could also be part of the system. The sunspace can have water or eutectic-salt thermal storage as well as a thermal mass floor.

Ventilating and Cooling

Sliding patio doors to the sunspaces and louvered entry doors can assist second floor windows in air intake. Plenums at the top of the south roof and an exhaust stack can expel uncomfortably warm indoor air when outdoor temperatures are favorable.

Conventional evaporative methods, reverse-cycle heat pumps, and air-conditioning can be used in part or whole for each unit. Evaporative mist sprays in the south patios can provide microclimatic cooling.

Features

The prefabricated energy-core modules are principal economical, functional, and structural centralized service elements. These two- and three-bedroom homes could be built and completed in much less time than conventionally built homes.

151

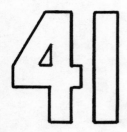

41

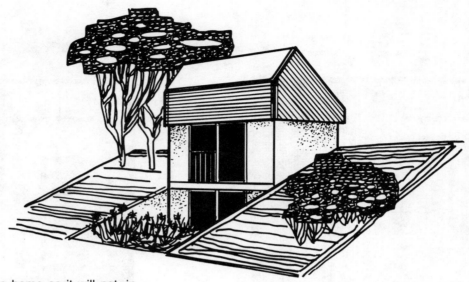

Design

Perhaps it is not fair to call this design a home as it will not, in most cases, meet the space provision or floor-to-floor access required by most building codes. However, it is the most ultracompact, affordable design of this book. The ladder between floors presents some hazard and inconvenience but does not require more-than-average agility. This design's principal attraction is its frugal land, materials, and labor requirements. It would be a really fun venture to build and live in and would make an ideal small addition to an existing residence. If connected to a two-story house, the ladder could be omitted and access could be provided from both levels of the existing home. The unit should appeal not only to the athletic person; a writer, artist, musician, or hobbyist could find it a delightful, undisturbed environment, as would an adolescent, young adult, or guest that might be included under a ladder-insurance clause.

Solar

Direct gain sunlight passing through south glazing to an intervening thermal mass floor (which could be supported by structural metal decking) can provide radiative energy with solar energy

242 Square Feet (22.5 Square Meters)

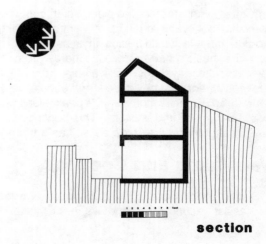

section

152

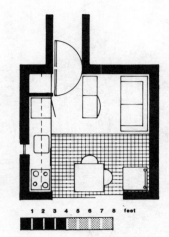

main floor

1 2 3 4 5 6 7 8 feet

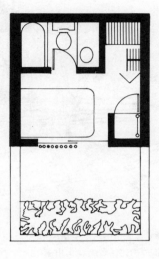

lower floor

storage to both levels of this unit. The solar orientation — as with all designs in this book — should be due south or not more than 20 degrees southeast or southwest from due south. Uncovered thermal mass concrete (or dark-tile-covered) floors can be direct gain thermal storage for either or both levels. Depending on the latitude of the site, the roof angle should be slanted to optimize the use of roof-mounted solar collectors for heating domestic hot water and, possibly, space. Insulated solar storage for the collectors can be located in an attic space structurally designed to support the weight or directly underground.

Ventilating and Cooling

The height of this unit favors inductive, temperature-differential, solar- and wind-assisted ventilation. Earth-sheltering, as illustrated, will favor natural cooling. A destratification fan and duct would be effective for circulating upper-level ceiling heat to the lower level. Suitable supplemental heating is described in the text.

Features

This ultracompact living unit can be built on a flat or south-, east-, or west-sloping site. It covers a minimal land area of only 12 x 12

feet (3.7 x 3.7 meters). The plan and design can be modified for duplex or clustering arrangements. It can be site built or be fabricated by a modular or mobile home manufacturer. Minimal site access is required for its erection. Its minimal cost might be met by cash or short-term financing.

The conceptual plan is readily expandable to 14 x 14 feet (4.3 x 4.3 meters), 16 x 16 feet (4.9 x 4.9 meters), 18 x 18 feet (5.5 x 5.5 meters), or greater dimensions based on a square. Large plan dimensions and stairways could meet minimal-dwelling code requirements.

The entry requires double-insulating doors against cold winter winds, but the doors should be designed to ventilate in summer. Clear, double-glazed, thermal-break, patio-type sliding doors for the lower and upper levels (with a protective railing on the upper level) are simple and inexpensive solutions for direct, thermal-gain daylighting, ventilating, and cooling.

Materials are at the options of the owner, designer, or builder. As with all these designs, consult the text for other functional and energy-conserving features.

153

Design

This ultracompact, two-level living unit offers a wide range of uses. It may not meet the minimal interior-space requirements of some building codes; however, it is likely that the swing towards affordable space-saving homes will change codes that have such unnecessary restrictions.

This living unit can serve as an ideal country, mountain, or seashore retreat; an urban free-standing or attached dwelling space; or as a low-cost, survival home. From fun and everyday livability to survival is a long stretch that can serve the old and sedentary, the young and lively, and any one or two persons living together with or without hobbies or artistic pursuits.

Solar

Passive solar direct gain is seasonally self-regulating. In winter, the south, southeast, or southwest orientation would receive welcome solar gains. In summer, the sloped glazing of clear plastic or glass (single, double, or double with high-transmissivity film) will be self-shaded. In spring, reflection from the glazing surface will increase as the sun's position elevates toward summer. Ground-mounted solar-thermosiphon collectors with or without a directly attached tank could heat domestic hot water.

345 Square Feet (32.1 Square Meters)

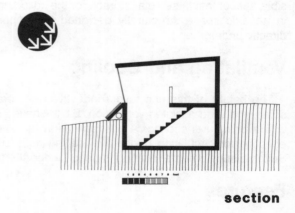

section

154

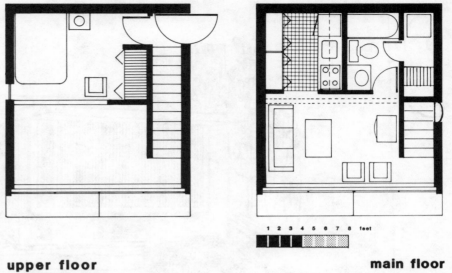

upper floor   **main floor**

Ventilating and Cooling

Ventilation is accomplished by a large, screened, horizontal conduit (treated against rusting) that would run laterally under the southside earth berm. Insulated, weather-stripped ventilation panels on the interior will allow air to enter at the floor line. The earth berm will, in summer and winter, favorably moderate the incoming air temperature. A high venting system to the north should be provided to exhaust the naturally convected air at the highest interior upper-level-ceiling point. Destratification provisions should also be made in cool-weather periods to circulate the upper, stratified ceiling air to the lower level.

As part of such a system, an underfloor gravel-filled plenum under a poured-concrete floor could act as a solar- and internal-thermal-storage mass. The heated air could be forced down a northside vertical duct with a quiet motorized blower, and the plenum would deliver radiant floor heat to the interior space and be slotted for return air at the south edge of the floor slab. Design of such a system should be by an architect, designer, or engineer experienced with passive and hybrid solar systems.

Features

This living unit possesses optimal livability within its small size. Its ground-coverage area is only 16 x 16 feet (4.9 x 4.9 meters). Space for a stacked washer-dryer and storage is provided under the stairway. The kitchen has generous pantry and dish-storage shelves within full-height, bifold-door cabinets. A high-low table can be adjusted in the living room to act as a lower cocktail table or higher dining table. An alternative would be a table located next to the stairway.

The open bedroom with solid railing overlooking the lower living space can be closed off with glass or plastic sliding panels for privacy. The proximity of the entry door should fulfill the bedroom escape requirements and provide required ventilation when equipped with an outer, louvered screen door. If building department officials fuss about required light, ventilation, and exiting, a window that meets these requirements can be provided.

155

462 Square Feet (42.9 Square Meters)

Design

This contemporary, straightforward, two-level habitat can be located on a narrow site. Earth-sheltering in the lower bedroom area stabilizes its temperature and provides a moderately cool, year-round environment.

The projecting cantilever of the upper-floor level and roof will provide summer shade over the lower window and upper glazing — essentially oriented toward the south. Its linear compact plan provides a spatial separation of living functions. Singles, couples, young, and old could find this an inexpensive residence.

Solar

The upper-level floor projects like a cantilever to allow space for solar-thermal storage. Vertical, double-wall, clear plastic glazing is usually more economical than glass. Direct gain, passive solar,

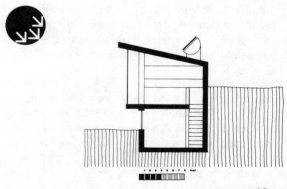

section

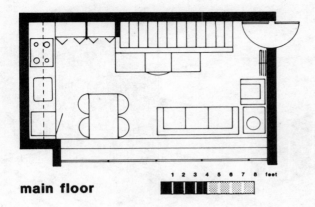

main floor

1 2 3 4 5 6 7 8 feet

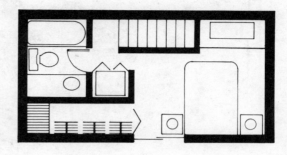

lower floor

interceptive, cabinet-type, selective-surface water storage or eutectic phase-change salts leave a defined living area relatively unaffected by direct solar radiation.

An active solar system for heating domestic hot water can be flat-plate or concentrating collectors located on the roof.

Ventilating and Cooling

An operable, side-sliding thermal-break window in the lower-level bedroom would not only vent the bedroom but, by convection through the upper level, would tend to cool the upper living space. A double-casement window and louvered entry door on the upper level would provide convective ventilation and cooling. Supplemental heat sources are described in the text.

Features

The lower level would occupy a site area of only 12 x 22 feet (3.7 x 6.7 meters) — the size of a single-car garage. The narrow interior-width ceiling, sloping downward to the north and the large glazed area to the south will produce a very luminous interior-living space. Vertical or horizontal blinds between the solar thermal-storage cabinet and the ceiling will aid control over daylight. Plumbing lines are integrated between floor levels. Connections for a stacked washer and dryer would be provided. The open space over the stairway (with a solid dry-walled railing) and the sloping ceiling will add to a feeling of openness.

157

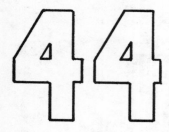

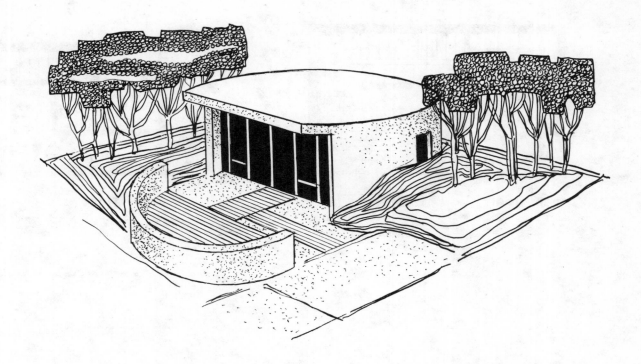

470 Square Feet (43.7 Square Meters)

Design

Circular forms seem protective and cozy. This plan in particular uses interior space well and avoids the struggle with partitions as well as furniture placement in the usual arrangement of pie-shaped interior-space divisions. The spaces are clearly defined and well oriented to the large south patio with its protective wall.

This unit can have many uses such as a vacation retreat; cabanas around a pool; a cluster of small homes surrounding a commons for play and recreation; executive suites at a conference center; studios for arts, music, or crafts; or, simply, individual living units in an urban, suburban, or primitive environment. It would be a fun kind of unit to build with insulated, compacted earth; concrete block; formed concrete; or treated, amputated telephone poles set on the circumference and treated with insulation and stucco.

Solar

The solar system is passive direct gain with a thermal mass floor for heat storage. Free-standing concentrators or other trough-form domestic-water solar heaters can be installed on the roof. The low profile of these units allows for solar access to other units in close proximity.

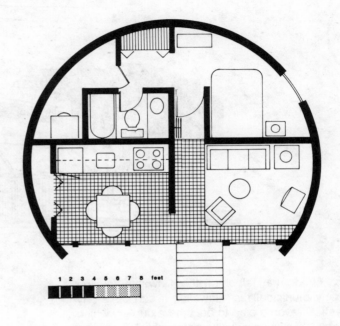

1 2 3 4 5 6 7 8 feet

Ventilating and Cooling

The greater the earth-sheltering, the more that the interior will remain cool in summer and warm in winter. The main-entrance sliding door; awning windows; and bedroom window close to or below grade will have a cooling and ventilating effect. The circular form will tend to accelerate interior ventilation as winds move around the form, creating a negative pressure. The front-roof overhang will provide summer shading.

Features

This home can be partially or full earth-sheltered, in which case ventilation and a light well would be needed for the bedroom window. The circular form with low external profile lends itself well to a developmental density of these units. The surface ratio to interior volume is small, thereby reducing cold-weather energy losses.

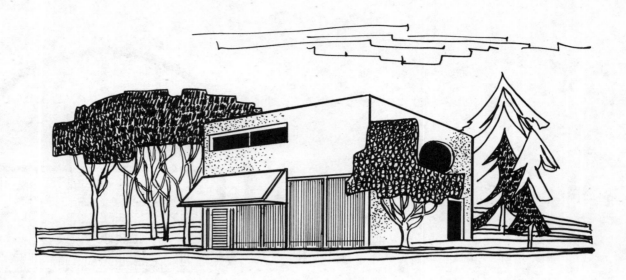

Design

This somewhat boxy abode may fall below the allowable housing square footage of many municipalities. However, it can be easily combined with an identical reverse plan to become a duplex, which may be more acceptable, as zoning density may permit.

To save space, this model has the inconvenience of a bathroom on a different level from the bedroom. It is a compact living unit suited to the energetic single or couple. As may be desired, the main-level bath could be reduced to a powder room, and an upstairs bathroom could be installed in part of the open space above the main-level living area.

Solar

A solid concrete or masonry wall painted black on the south side about 4 feet (1.2 meters) high, calculated in thickness to meet thermal mass requirements, and slotted at the bottom for circulation of air between the southern glazing would act as solar-thermal storage. Alternative masses could be water tubes or eutectic salts. The south-facing canopy that extends over the entry is a sloping surface that could accommodate flat-plate collectors for heating domestic hot water.

480 Square Feet (44.6 Square Meters)

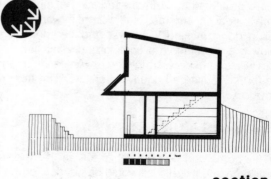

section

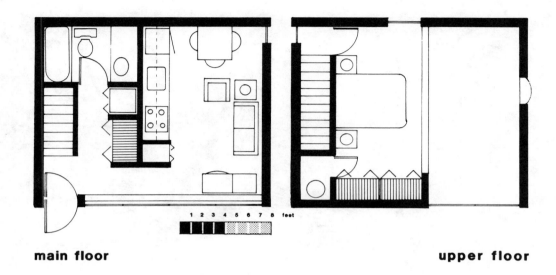

main floor

1 2 3 4 5 6 7 8 feet

upper floor

Ventilating and Cooling

The high-ceiling portion of the interior space above the main-level living area lends itself well to natural ventilation. Dampered, roof wind turbines are most available, but other natural-exhaust roof caps can be more efficient. Full-height casement and awning-type windows allow outdoor air to enter for cooling and ventilating. Inasmuch as refrigeration, cooking, lights, and body heat will especially escalate interior temperatures in the small interior volume, supplemental heating requirements will be less than for substantially larger units.

Features

The design simplicity of the exterior allows it to be unobtrusively attached to an existing residence or as a freestanding living unit. Color has a great influence on the strength of the architectural form. Natural colors or colors that blend into the surrounding environment de-emphasize the architecture. Closet space, including space under and over the stairway, is generous for so small a dwelling. The 30-inch (76-centimeter) -deep kitchen cabinets and stacked washer and dryer add to the livability.

The double door is a practical answer to the thermal losses experienced through and around doors. See the description in the text. Through the various seasons, internal or external solar shading control will be necessary to avoid overheating in the main-level living spaces.

Design

This earth-sheltered, single-level floor plan has a small loft accessible by a ladder that can be placed at an angle for easier access. Young couples, singles, seniors, guests, a couple with a visiting child, or a mother- or father-in-law can be accommodated with reasonable privacy and comfort. The south entry with protective roof reduces wintertime energy loss and would provide entry protection in rainy areas. With a little modification, the units could be made into duplexes, condominiums, or townhomes.

It would also be a delightful free-standing guest, vacation, or retreat house.

Solar

The passive solar sunspace can be used for numerous space functions or for food production. The inner glass sliding doors can receive secondary solar gains. Passive solar gains can be received directly into a thick (preferably 6 inch [15 centimeter]) concrete floor.

If a hot tub is decided upon, a transparent cover can be put on the water for direct passive solar gains. Active solar roof collectors that heat the hot tub would also heat domestic hot water. The

498 Square Feet (46.3 Square Meters)

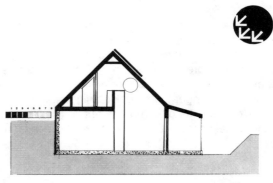

section

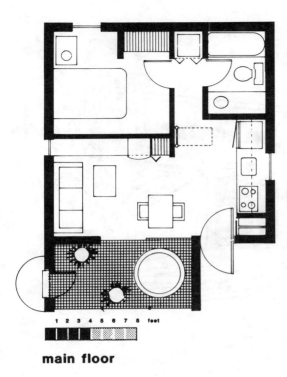

main floor

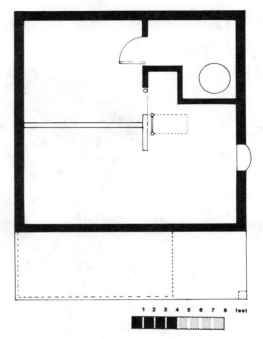

upper floor

sunspace can serve numerous purposes, such as greenhouse; indoor winter sunbathing; clothes drying; materials outgassing; food drying; dining; party overflow from the living space; hobbies; a visiting-child's play space; and solar cooking and heating.

Ventilating and Cooling

The roof form lends itself well to effective ventilation near the ridge and for destratification. A louvered, screened opening with inner, insulated, weather-stripped doors vents and cools the sunspace and, with the side-sliding door open, the interior living spaces. Energy-conserving double- or triple-glazed casement windows can be used to ventilate and cool the living and bedroom areas. An awning window could fit under the upper kitchen cabinets. Supplemental heating systems are described in the text.

Features

This design offers an unusual amount of security as well as low maintenance. Thirty-inch (76-centimeter) -deep base kitchen cabinets are not standard but should be. The pantry behind the entry door has food storage racks that slide out. The upper cabinets will satisfy additional needs. Storage is also available in the loft space. The stacked washer and dryer, bath, and kitchen keep plumbing lines together.

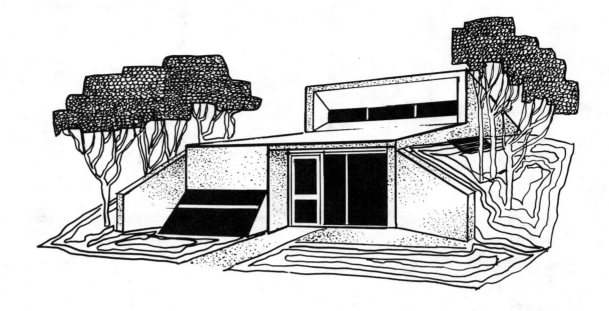

Design

Cataclysmic natural disasters or the unhappy possibility of a nuclear catastrophe could make partial or complete self-sufficiency necessary. This underground, concrete, insulated survival dwelling will provide a level of protection. Security panels could be provided for the clerestory and south windows. It is advised that a complete outer wrap of adequate insulation be applied and finished with a heavily reinforced nylon mesh-acrylic coating.

Solar

A self-contained thermosiphon solar collector and water storage can serve domestic hot water needs. The south-facing, direct gain, eutectic-salt, thermal-storage bunker can provide radiant heat for the living area. The south-facing clerestory can provide daylighting and solar radiation to an insulated, northside, exposed concrete wall and concrete floor (preferably covered with dark tile) for solar thermal storage. A destratification fan would tend to equalize the interior distribution of heat and relocate solar and internal heat in the northeast rock-bin storage.

460 Square Feet (42.7 Square Meters)

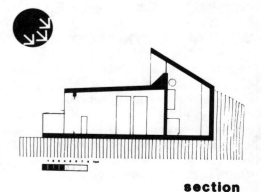

section

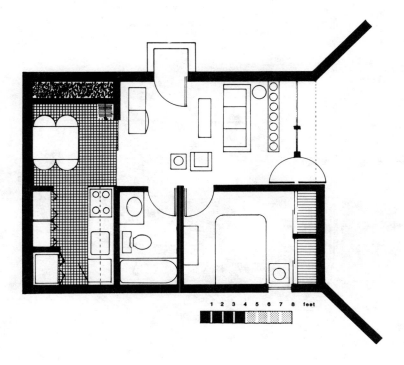

1 2 3 4 5 6 7 8 feet

Ventilating and Cooling

Natural airflow ventilation is provided by windows, louvered-screen panels, an eastside, sunken earth pit with operable ventilation, and louvered entry door. Cool nocturnal air can, during evening hours, cool the house and the rock-bin storage. The below-grade, outer concrete walls should be insulated, but the earth's temperatures would tend to stabilize indoor temperatures at a comfort level.

Features

It is important that an insulative thermal break be provided where the concrete wing walls meet the building structure. Sliding doors that separate the dining room and kitchen can serve to make that area a thermal retreat space.

Design

This high-level-security, underground house can be easily buttoned up against severe weather or intruders. Such enclosure would also provide substantial thermal protection. The outer barred but ventilated entry door would also offer security. The massive concrete inner partition walls provide a heavy-matrix, temperature-stabilizing mass. The roof is completely earth covered.

Solar

Direct solar gains in the living area are stored in a eutectic-salt bunker and portions of thermal mass floor. An array of solar collectors is located on the roof for domestic hot water. A small wood, coal, or oil heater is indicated for emergency heating and cooking.

484 Square Feet (45 Square Meters)

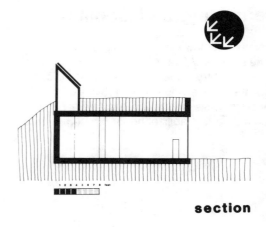

section

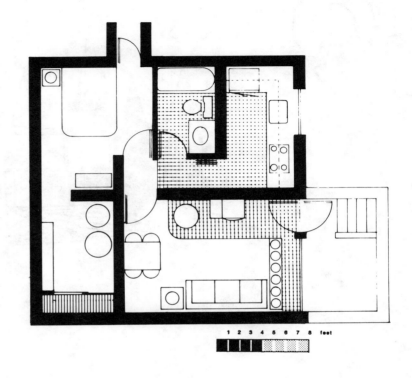

1 2 3 4 5 6 7 8 feet

Ventilating and Cooling

Ventilation is by means of the outer security door, vent door from the master bedroom, and kitchen window. This cross ventilation and the earth-coupling of the house should be sufficient for cooling in most climates.

Features

The shielded store room can hold an extensive inventory of provisions. The solar and hot water tank can serve emergency water needs. The bedroom and bath are shielded from possible radiation. An escape and ventilation exit is provided from the bedroom. Reinforced-concrete roof spans would be minimal because of interior concrete partitions.

572 Square Feet (53.1 Square Meters)

Design

This is another underground survival home. Good surface drainage, control over underground water, careful and complete waterproofing, and insulation of outer concrete walls and roof are essential. Heavily constructed and insulative operable security panels should be provided for all window openings. Exterior, heavy acrylic coating should be applied over nylon mesh, over appropriate insulative board. This design provides for a higher level of radiation protection and a secondary retreat space for temporary sleeping and living as a fallout shelter.

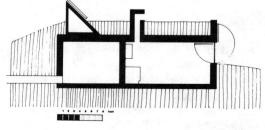

section

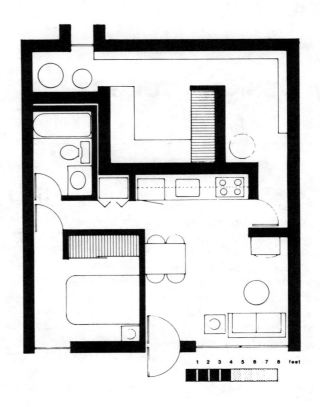

Solar

South-facing windows are too small to provide substantial direct passive solar gain; however, the array of solar collectors mounted on the roof can supply space and domestic hot water heating. An emergency stove for cooking and heating is indicated with both combustion and fresh-air requirements.

Ventilating and Cooling

Side-sliding double-glazed windows can provide ventilation along with a flue and ventilation tower. In normal use, ventilation is by screened side-sliding windows. Cooling is by earth coupling and thermal mass of the building structures.

Features

Solar- and domestic-heated water tanks are available in the shelter for emergency use. A double, protective entry door can be provided. Extensive shelving can serve for longer periods of shelter use. All living needs can be well organized and inventoried by this arrangement.

Appendix A

Energy Design Process

The plans and designs presented in this book are conceptual and nontechnical. Publications that offer rules of thumb and various methodologies for determining the size, intrinsic properties, and systemic relationships of architecture with its energy components are listed in the reference section. Standardized passive solar plans and designs generally have the drawback of not fitting to definitive energy-zone characteristics or to unique site conditions and factors specific to each project.

Long-term as well as immediate energy trade-offs between function, economics, and human response and interaction are critical to design. In particular, compact, affordable, solar and energy-conserving designs have to be more sensitively conceived, planned, designed, and developed than those for conventional dwellings. The total integrative-energy, functional, and aesthetic interaction of a project with its community should not be overlooked.

Experience, intuition, integrative endeavor, and common sense that value the *whole* (through time and space) should remain as denominators of creative and energy-effective design.

Passive Solar System Design and Storage

Many different formulas and methods have been developed for sizing passive solar heating systems. Rules of thumb have been developed by J. Douglas Balcomb and colleagues at the Los Alamos Scientific Laboratory in New Mexico and others and include those set forth by Edward Mazria in his book, *The Passive Solar Energy Book.* These rules of thumb are intended to be used during the schematic design phase of a project (early in the design process) to give rough ideas about relative sizes and amounts of solar glazing and thermal storage needed for a particular design situation.

Orientation. "The orientation of the solar glazing should lie between 20 degrees east and 32 degrees west of true south."[54] Balcomb notes that some designers might prefer an orientation a bit east of south to "wake up" the building early in the morning.

[54]U.S. Department of Energy, *Passive Solar Design Analysis,* prepared by J. Douglas Balcomb, *Passive Solar Design Handbook,* vol. 2 (Springfield, Va.: National Technical Information Service, U.S. Dept. of Commerce, 1980), p. 28.

However, in southerly latitudes where summer overheating is a problem, Balcomb suggests that east and west orientations be avoided. Also, he states that a local shading situation, such as shade from trees or other buildings, could warrant departure from the rule of thumb.[55] When determining orientation, it is important to remember that due to the earth's magnetic field, magnetic north can vary by a number of degrees east or west from true north depending upon location. A magnetic declination map or a surveyor should be consulted.

Direct Gain Solar Systems. Direct gain systems are those in which solar radiation directly enters interior space and preferably heats a thermal mass. The thermal mass (depending upon its color and other properties) sustains the heat for an extended period of time and reduces short-term overheating of the space. Solar radiation that passes through an inner glazing of a solar, direct gain space provides a secondary gain to the inner space. External and internal energy diversities will condition solar behavior. The design resolution should not lose sight of the innumerable elements that

[55]Ibid., p. 29

affect energy performance. The most exacting calculations cannot define all of the interactive energy responses and all envisioned alternatives should be weighed.

Clerestories. Clerestory windows or skylights can be used to admit direct solar gain into a space through the roof. The ceiling of the clerestory should be a light color to reflect and diffuse sunlight down into the space and provide direct radiation for thermal collection or storage. The exterior roof surface can be reflective to substantially increase solar gains. A tilted, overhead reflector (in the equinox position) above the clerestory can also substantially increase solar gains. The tilted reflector should be designed to shade the clerestory glazing area in summer but optimize solar gains in winter.

Skylights are significant energy losers in cold climates. Glazing, size, and location should be carefully selected to favor daylight but minimize interior energy loss. Appropriate shading and light control should be provided as needed. Exterior and/or interior reflectors can be used with skylights to increase solar gains in winter. The author has invented a Skyshaft that projects high above the roof line at a south-facing angle and is used to optimize direct and indirect solar daylight. The Skyshaft is compartmented with air spaces to greatly reduce internal energy losses. Such devices are small but effective.

Thermal-Storage Mass with Direct Gain. Solar gains can be stored for later use in the evening and to prevent daytime overheating. The most commonly used materials for thermal mass are concrete, masonry, water, and eutectic salts. When using concrete or masonry for thermal-storage mass:

- the thickness of interior concrete or masonry walls and floors is critical to thermal response;
- glazing patterns affect the response of thermal mass to direct and indirect solar radiation;
- it is best to use dark-colored thermal mass floors;
- medium to dark colors are appropriate for thermal mass walls;
- thermal mass walls should not have pictures and wall hangings; and
- thermal mass floors should not have rugs, carpeting, or furniture that shades a large area.

When using water or eutectic-salt thermal-storage mass:

- locate the water or eutectic-salt containers to receive direct sun from 9:00 A.M. to 3:00 P.M.;
- the water or eutectic-salt container exposed to direct sunlight should be a dark color, or the water can be dyed dark in a transparent or translucent container; and
- the thermal mass of the water or eutectic salts should be proportioned to the glazing area.

Remote Thermal Storage. Numerous schemes are conceptually illustrated using remote thermal storage. In temperate and cold climates with either sporadic or inadequate wintertime solar radiation, either low-temperature (direct radiative or convective) or well-insulated and well-controlled higher-temperature storage can use the sun's energy more effectively. A particular benefit is that heat provided by solar radiation can be located in the most advantageous interior positions — usually under the lowest central or northside area. In this manner, the most effective interior use of solar gains can be realized. Such remote thermal storage can be charged by a thermosiphon-solar collector heat-flow method or by means of a hybrid system. The hybrid system can make use of the highest, ceiling-level, stratified air (concentrated from internal and residual solar-heat gains) to combine with the solar heat gain from a sunspace, solar collection in the attic, direct-solar-exposed ductwork, or by other means. Generally, a fan or blower is required. Economic photovoltaic energy will likely replace the need for electric power for the operation of such equipment in the future.

Passive Solar Heating Calculations Methodology. The most widely used current method for analyzing the performance of typical passive solar homes and buildings and predicting the monthly auxiliary heat requirement — the SLR (solar load ratio) method — was developed at the Los Alamos National Laboratory by J. Douglas Balcomb and others. Two volumes produced by the Los Alamos group for the U.S. Department of Energy contain data concerning this method:

Passive Solar Design Handbook Volume 2: Passive Solar Design Analysis is available from the National Technical Information Service (NTIS), 5285 Port Royal Road, Springfield, Virginia 22161.

Passive Solar Design Handbook Volume 3: Passive Solar Design Analysis is available through the American Solar Energy Society, 1230 Grandview Ave., Boulder, Colorado 80302 or the U.S. Superintendent of Documents,

U.S. Government Printing Office, Washington, D.C. 20402.
The third volume contains data for 219 cities in the United States and Canada with 94 passive solar system differentiations, versus six basic reference designs in Volume 2 (both volumes are necessary, however, because Volume 3 does not replace the preceding volume).

Primary information concerning the building's heat loss and south glazing area is needed to use this methodology. Solar calculations for determining thermal mass and assessing other factors using the SLR method are particularly appropriate for the small, single or double passive solar systems used in the presented plans and designs in this book.

Active Solar System Design of Liquid- and Air-Type Systems

Orientation. Optimally, it is due south; however, this can vary up to 25 degrees east or west with only a small loss in performance.[56]

Tilt. The collector tilt angle is determined as follows:
- for building space heating only, the general rule of thumb is latitude plus 15 degrees; and
- for domestic hot water heating only, the optimum tilt angle is latitude plus 5 degrees.

These angles may not apply in all situations and other considerations, such as architectural integration, seasonal heating load distribution, ease of assembly, and maintenance, etc. may be more important than maximizing performance. Variations of 15 to 20 degrees will still give over 90 percent of the maximum possible insolation.[57]

Storage. Usually, for domestic water heating (depending on the system and the manufacturer) a water-drainback solar collection system will be more efficient than a water-glycol or oil (silicone or hydrocarbon) fluid heat-transfer system. Some manufacturers have developed totally integrated, solar-heated domestic hot water systems with collectors and tank with drainback capability as a complete package.

Such liquid solar systems usually use a preheat or specially adapted thermal-storage tank. By adding more solar collection area (or intensifying reflectors) above that normally needed for domestic hot water heating, partial or more complete space heating can be accomplished.

The sizing and design of the active, liquid-type solar system for space heating should not neglect passive solar or hybrid-thermal contributions.

Air-type solar collection systems are generally used for interior space heating. Their advantage is that they do not freeze up in winter. They can directly use the hottest, stratified air for space heating from rock-bin storage and transfer stored heat to air at relatively low temperatures. More operational energy is required for air-handling blowers than for that required for the pumps used in liquid systems and ductwork for air distribution is more space demanding than piping.

Both liquid- and air-type solar collection systems, when architectural planning and design permit, can be thermosiphon (without mechanical assistance). The situation appropriate for thermosiphoning seldom occurs except for domestic hot water heating.

Data on the design and sizing of active system collector arrays and sizing of thermal storage can be found in many publications, including *Introduction to Solar Technology* by Fisk and Anderson (see references).

---

[56]Bruce Anderson. *The Solar Home Book: Heating, Cooling, and Designing with the Sun* (Harrisville, N.H.; Cheshire Books, 1976), p. 174.

[57]Ibid., p. 176.

Recommended Insulation Levels

...ure the degree of resist-...ial to heat flow and are ...ing insulating values. The ...lue rating of a material, the ...sulating properties. U-value ... of the coefficient of heat transfer, or how much heat will flow through a given construction assembly. It is equal to the reciprocal of the R-factor; i.e., U = 1/R. For example, R-40 = U-0.025.

Table 2 lists the recommended insulation for various levels of commonly available insulation materials. Do not use ureaformaldehyde foam insulation: it was banned by the Consumer Product Safety Commission. Formaldehyde causes respiratory ailments and other illness and is suspected of causing nasal passage cancer.

Table 1: Insulation Thicknesses (in Inches)

R-Value	Batts or Blankets		Loose Fill (Poured-in)			Rigid Plastic Foams	
	Glass Fiber	Rock Wool	Glass Fiber	Rock Wool	Cellulose Fiber	Urethane	Styrene
R-11	3½-4	3	5	4	3	1½	2¼
R-13	4	4½	6	4½	3½	2	2¾
R-19	6-6½	5¼	8-9	6-7	5	2¾	4¼
R-22	6½	6	10	7-8	6	3	4½
R-26	8	8½	12	9	7-7½	3¾	5½
R-30	9½-10½	9	12-13	10-11	8	4½	6½
R-33	11	10	15	11-12	9	4¾	7¼
R-38	12-13	10½	17-18	13-14	10-11	5½	8½

SOURCE: *Insulation Fact Sheet.*[58]

[58]National Solar Heating and Cooling Information Center, *Insulation Fact Sheet*, DC 101. (Rockville, Md.: NSHCIC, 1977), p. 3.

Fig. 181. Heating Zone Map

Table 2: Heating Zone Chart

Heating Zone	R-Value of Insulation Recommended for:		
	Ceiling	Wall	Floor
0, 1	26	13	11
2	26	19	13
3	30	19	19
4	33	19	22
5	38	19	22

NOTE: Values are presented in generalized figures. Insulation should be tailored to specific site conditions and could also vary from the recommended amounts because of a building's construction materials or style or if superinsulation is desired.

SOURCE: *Insulation Fact Sheet.*

Appendix C
Insulative Properties of Various Materials

Table 3: Insulative Properties of Various Materials

Insulation Material	Thickness (in Inches)	R-Value
Fiberglass (board)	1	R-4.00
Fiberglass (batt)	3½	R-11.00
Fiberglass (batt)	6	R-19.00
Rockwool (batt)	3	R-11.00
Rockwool (batt)	5¼	R-19.00
Rockwool (loose)	1	R-4.00
Expanded polystyrene	1 (varying densities)	R-4.00 to R-5.26
Molded polystyrene beads (beadboard)	1	R-3.57
Expanded urethane	1	R-6.25
Cellulose	1	R-3.70
Hardwood (maple, oak)	1	R-0.91
Softwood (fir, pine)	1	R-1.25
Plywood	½	R-0.62
Concrete	1	R-0.08
Brick	1	R-0.20
Gypsum board (drywall)	½	R-0.45

NOTE: For the R-value of movable insulation, check manufacturers' data.

SOURCES: ASHRAE, pp. 22. 13-22.17; *Insulation Fact Sheet*.

Appendix D
Physical Properties of Various Heat Storage Materials

Table 4: Physical Properties of Various Heat Storage Materials

Heat Storage Materials	Specific Heat Btu/lb (deg F)	Density lb/cu.ft.	Heat Capacity by Volume Btu/cu.ft. (deg F)	Thermal Conductivity Btuh/sq. ft. (deg F/ft)
Water	0.999 (68F)	62.32 (68F)	62.25	0.348
Concrete (stone)	0.156 (392F)	144	22.46	0.54
Rock pebbles	0.21	100	21.0	
Fireclay brick	0.198 (212F)	112	22.18	0.58 (392F)
Magnesite brick	0.222 (212F)	158	35.08	2.2 (400F)
Adobe	0.24	106	25.44	0.3
Earth (dry and packed)		95		0.037
Quarried stone	0.2	95		

NOTE: Values are at room temperature unless otherwise noted.

SOURCES: ASHRAE, pp. 37.2-37.4; Mazria, p. 340; Fisk, Marian Jacobs and Anderson, H.C. William, *Introduction to Solar Technology* (Reading, Mass.: Addison-Wesley Publishing Company, 1982), p. 110.

Appendix E

Reflectivity of Surfaces

Appendix F

Climatic Exterior Paint Colors

Table 5: Reflectivity of Surfaces

Surface	Percentage
White paint	75-80
Grey paint	25
Flat black paint	4
Aluminum paint	60-70
Polished aluminum	75-85
Polished aluminum (optical quality)	85-95
Concrete	40
White marble chips	45

SOURCES: Anderson, p. 83; *IES Lighting Handbook: 1981 Reference Volume* (New York: Illuminating Engineering Society of North America, 1981), p. 7-10.

Table 6: Climatic Exterior Paint Colors

Paint Colors for Roof and Walls	Climatic Conditions				
	Cold Winters Hot Summers	Cold Winters Moderate Summers	Cold Winters Cool Summers	Moderate Winters Moderate Summers	Warm Winters Hot Summers
Dark Color Roof			X		
Dark Color Walls	X	X	X		
Medium Color Roof		X		X	
Medium Color Walls				X	
Light Color Roof	X				X
Light Color Walls					X

NOTE: Climatic characteristics vary greatly from one geographic area to another. Within each area careful consideration has to be given to these differences, and colors selected accordingly. As examples, Denver, Colorado, has cold winters and moderate summer temperatures. Dryness makes the climate more tolerable. Chicago, Illinois, has cold winters and hot summers. Humidity contributes to summer discomfort. Phoenix, Arizona, has warm winters and hot summers. Dryness through all seasons contributes to year-round comfort.

Regional Climatic Zones and Guidelines

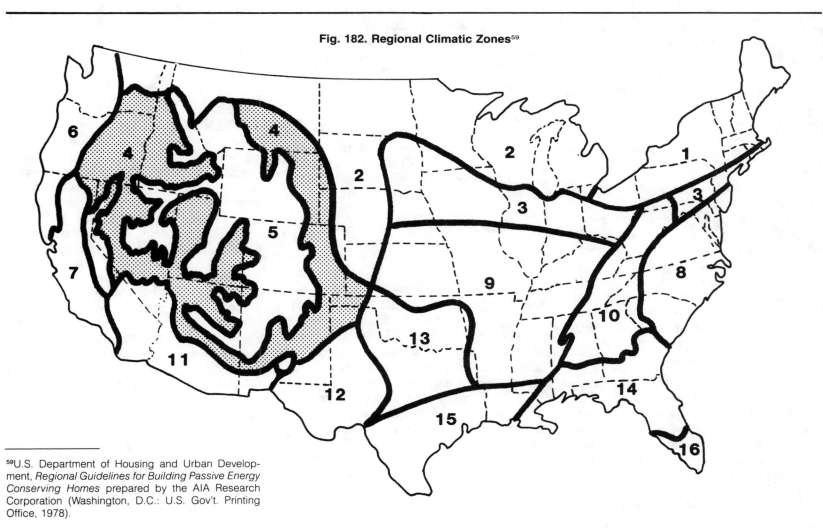

Fig. 182. Regional Climatic Zones[59]

---

[59]U.S. Department of Housing and Urban Development, *Regional Guidelines for Building Passive Energy Conserving Homes* prepared by the AIA Research Corporation (Washington, D.C.: U.S. Gov't. Printing Office, 1978).

Guidelines for Heating

1. New England. Extreme winter temperatures must be blocked out, heat held in; use compact forms with snug floor plans to minimize exposure; use earth to insulate; build homes together to share heat; insulate roof heavily; use buffer spaces; double and triple glazing, exterior window shutters; wind protection with evergreens and fences on the north and west; long, sloping roofs into the wind; protect doors, use air-locked entries; solid-core or insulated doors and storm doors; elongate only on east-west axis; full southern exposure, winter sun penetration to interior living spaces; direct gain sunspace with mass; prevent infiltration losses; weather-strip and caulk all openings.

2. North Central. Keep heat in, cold out by building into the earth, partially underground, or with earth berms, with entries lower than living spaces; air locks; build adjoining homes; site against north slopes with south exposure; deflect winds over; use compact forms; buffer spaces on north; insulated south windows for solar gain; attached sunspaces; heavy, massive construction for time-lag heating; protect against infiltration; increase thermal resistance of roofs, walls with insulation.

3. Midwest. Keep heat in, cold out by using small, compact forms, attached housing, good insulation, and weather stripping; site into the earth (earth-shelter), use earth berms; reduce window area (except to the south), especially on the north; double or triple glazing, insulated shutters; coniferous wind breaks; buffer spaces; garage on northwest; air locks and vestibules; open-to-winter-sun living spaces on south; greenhouses, thermosiphoning air collectors, direct gain; thermal mass in central and/or peripheral location; heavy insulation for roof and north walls.

4. Great Plains. Open to sun for winter heating by using direct gain, attached sunspaces, or greenhouses; reflective materials on ground by south windows; guard from winter winds by clustering buildings, minimizing architectural surface, maximizing volume; low profile on exposed sites; garages and secondary spaces as buffer spaces; earth berms, heavy evergreens on north and west; air-lock entries; insulated windows; massive materials for time-lag heating with continuous insulation on outside; if using wood stoves, surround with mass, place in center of house, use outside combustion air; heavy shrubs next to walls for insulation; underground construction.

5. Alpine. Keep heat in, cold out; minimize perimeter surface areas, cluster functions tightly; heavy insulation around entire perimeter, earth berming, or underground construction; nestle into the site, buffer spaces on wind exposures; double or triple glazing with night insulation; minimize outside doors, use air locks or vestibules protected from the wind with wingwalls and roofs; avoid thermal bridging on external walls; locate thermal mass in the center of the house; avoid sites at the bottom of a valley with cold air drainage; open south to the sun and use heavy, massive walls with dark color and rough texture; use snow fences and wind breaks to keep snow away from entries; direct and secondary solar gains; build on north slopes facing south; be careful not to block winter sun angles.

6. Northwest Pacific Coast. Heat in and cold out by insulating exterior walls; earth berms; earth-shelter construction; use compact forms; limit window areas, especially on north walls; double-glazed windows with insulation; common-wall, clustered buildings; site above fog zone on south-facing slopes when possible; light-colored surfaces to reflect sun into the house; open to the sun with interior thermal mass, direct gain; shelter from wind and site in middle of slopes, landscape plantings and hedgerows as shelter belts; angled roof to deflect winds; air-lock entries; protect against infiltration; wood an appropriate building material.

7. California Central Valley, Southern Coast. Open to sun to provide winter heating; elongate east-west, expose to south; site on south, southeast, or southwest slopes when possible; do not violate solar access; direct gain; interior thermal mass to augment time-lag heating; shelter from cold winds with plantings, protected doors and windows; insulation to reduce heat loss.

8. Mid-Atlantic Coast. Insulate from cold by using earth berms, building into sloping grades; buffer spaces on exterior walls; minimal exterior surface area, compact floor plans; night insulation or thermal-response glazing on windows; open to sun; use direct gain, greenhouses or sun-rooms; protect from winter winds and infiltration; use heavy construction and thermal mass in areas with large diurnal swings; cautious underground construction; zone for smaller living space in winter.

9. Mississippi Valley. Protect against consistently cool winter temperatures; compact floor plans, minimal outside surface area; centralized thermal mass; internal zoning with buffer spaces; avoid thermal bridges with continuous thermal barriers; good insulation; provide heat storage mass, open to sun; sunspace; avoid infiltration, provide wind barriers, air locks, or vestibules; build into hillside; insulate glass areas.

10. Appalachia. Against cool to cold temperatures, nestle into site; continuous exterior insulation; buffer spaces; window insulation; use massive construction materials for time-lag heating; sunspaces with mass; direct gain, open-to-the-south winter sun; build into south-facing hillsides; protect from winter winds with landscaping and tight construction; shelter doors with wing-walls and screens or use air locks; earth berms; insulate house surround.

11. Southwest Desert. Protect from winter temperatures with exterior insulation; seal against infiltration; earth berming and underground construction very good; use large thermal mass within house and heavy thermal-lag exterior south, east, and west walls; orient house to winter sun for time-lag heating; compact forms.

12. West Texas. In cool and cold temperatures, let sun in; site house to avoid shading south walls; use direct gain, attached sunspaces; cluster buildings to prevent heat loss; use window insulation; earth berming or underground construction; use massive materials inside and outside; heavy roof construction; time-lag heating; protect from cold winter winds and infiltration; buffer spaces; good insulation important.

13. Panhandle, Central Texas, Oklahoma. Allow for winter sun penetration; provide internal and external thermal mass; attach sunspaces; use extensive mass for time-lag heating; use earth-to-air heat exchangers; insulate window areas; protect from winter winds with buffer spaces; design building shape and configuration to help alleviate wind stress in winter; protect entries; reduce infiltration with well-fitted doors and windows; weather stripping.

14. Bayou Country. Use mass to smooth diurnal swings; underground construction, using care in regard to drainage and moisture; provide for maximum solar access in winter; create sun-rooms for winter use only; add mass to sunspaces; avoid cold air infiltration, drafts; elevate thresholds, well-fitting doors and windows; shutters or air-tight curtains.

15. Texas Gulf Coast (Mild Winters). Stop winter infiltration; tight window and door openings; buffer spaces on north; deflect winds with earth berms, siting into slopes; allow for winter sun; sunspace, sun-porches for winter use; avoid exposure to cold temperatures; internal zoning.

16. Southern Florida and Hawaii. Let in sun at selected times for heating; sun-rooms for winter use; sunspace thermal mass walls; avoid exposure to cold temperatures; zone internal spaces for protection; compact forms that still allow air movement; some thermal mass could be beneficial.

Guidelines for Cooling

1. New England. Protect from summer sun by shading with deciduous trees, fixed shading devices, shading for spring and fall also; cross ventilation in spring, summer, and fall when warm or hot; shade and ventilate sunspaces as required; ventilate the attic; mold and mildew problem reduced by ventilation also; allow natural ventilation but not winter infiltration; capture summer breezes; add on outside living spaces; older homes used inductive ventilation with louvered or glass-enclosed belvederes; can use direct cooling with water bodies (lakes or ponds) using a heat exchanger; also springs or wells can cool food (spring house, well house); interseasonal ice storage possible.

2. North Central. Protect from sun with overhangs with operable louvers; deciduous trees; shutters on east and west facades; shading devices such as lowered awnings or canopies; earth-shelter and underground construction good for this region; vernacular houses had sod roofs; use massive materials, increase thermal resistance of walls and roofs; flatten diurnal temperature swings and provide time-lag cooling; seasonal ice storage possible; also cooling by heat pump transfer from shallow ponds or lakes; heat exchanger for deeper water.

3. Midwest. Keep hot temperatures out with adequate insulation (heavy for roof and north walls); caulking and weather stripping to make house tight; reflective roofs and nonreflective ground cover; dark-colored walls except on west; earth-shelter and earth berming beneficial; underground construction best; protect from sun with shading devices with air space for ventilation; shading on east and west; deciduous trees; vernacular prairie houses had deep overhangs, particularly for bedrooms where good ventilation with coolness needed at night; walls should be shaded during the day; Frank Lloyd Wright used strips of windows below overhangs near the ceiling for ventilation, but this increases heat losses in winter; cross ventilation, air movement important; operable or louvered windows; high vents for inductive ventilation; porches open to south breezes; augmentation with whole-house fans; exhaust or pressurization systems; good attic ventilation; humidity problem makes cooling difficult and causes a greater need for mechanical and refrigeration cooling; fans, air-conditioning, dehumidifiers; use of desiccants to remove moisture a possibility.

4. Great Plains. Evaporative cooling; locate pools of water or fountains in house or in path of incoming breezes; mist sprays; roof sprays; vegetation; evaporative roof ponds; mechanical evaporative coolers; protect from the sun with ventilated shading, shading on east and west, overhangs; cross ventilation and inductive ventilation; solar chimneys, stack action, ventilation with thermal mass; wind turbines; solar plenums; ridge vents; extended roof on west; exposed glass can use clear and heat-absorbing glazing in an envelope that will ventilate off heat; nocturnal cooling; night flushing with cool air; earth-shelter; massive materials, thermal mass for time-lag cooling; radiative cooling possible; subterranean aquifers can be used with heat pumps or heat exchanger economizer cycle on air-conditioning to bring in outdoor air for cooling when temperatures allow.

5. Alpine. Nocturnal cooling by "flushing" inductive ventilation; solar collectors can be used to assist inductive flow; shading devices; deep shading over west exposures; shading out away from the building, such as solar screens; reflective movable insulation on windows; pressure system with

forced air can bring in outside air for cooling; mass for time-lag cooling.

6. Pacific Northwest. Air movement, cross ventilation; air through attics and crawl spaces that avoids wood rot; open to catch ocean breezes; wind direction vane on ventilators to prevent downdrafts; not too much shading is needed because of high percentage of cloud cover, except in inland areas with clearer skies or at higher elevations; easy-to-grow vegetation for shading; roof and walls can be a moderate color; outside decks are common.

7. California Central Valley and Southern Coast. Interior thermal mass, well-reinforced, used with night ventilation; cross ventilation; ventilated attics and crawl spaces; ventilated and shaded outdoor spaces; arcades, courtyard plans; shaded patios; shading is important; vegetation on houses; moderately light-colored roof, light-colored exterior walls; red, Spanish-tile roof with ventilating air spaces; evaporative cooling: pools, ponds, mist and spray heads, vegetation in path of incoming air, roof ponds, fountains; radiative cooling possible with mass.

8. Mid-Atlantic Coast. Air movement important, well-ventilated attics and basements; covered porches to catch prevailing winds; inductive ventilation, as much stack action as possible by using high ceilings, venting living spaces through stairways and roof belvederes; cross ventilation: louvered shutters and doors, open plans; elevated living spaces; floor system on piers in

southern part of region; sun protection: ventilated shading; vertical shading on east and west; light-colored roofs and walls; vines and vegetation on houses; well-insulated houses; earth berming and underground construction possible, but with caution due to high water table, plentiful rain; avoid extra humidity, careful placement of vegetation; effectively ventilate kitchens, baths, laundry.

9. Mississippi Valley. Maximize air movement: cross ventilation, open interior planning, extendable porches on all sides; continuous corridors; elevated houses; ventilated attics and roofs; open transoms and doors between rooms; louvered shutters running to floor over opening for ventilation and privacy; high ceilings and inductive air flow; sun and heat protection; good insulation, reflective roof, nonreflective ground cover; deep overhangs; outside porches and porticoes for shading and water protection under building; shading devices; some mass inside house to aid cooling; avoid moisture, extra humidity; good drainage; build on higher ground; remove plants from direct sun to reduce evaporation; mechanical cooling with ground-water heat pump.

10. Appalachia. Natural ventilation, cross ventilation; well-ventilated attics, basements, and crawl spaces; central hall plans with high ceilings to vent out; porches and outdoor living spaces; siting to catch prevailing winds; elevated spaces; light-colored or metal reflective roofs; shading with vegetation, exterior devices; minimize east and west exposures; good insulation; mass for time-lag cooling; avoid extra humidity with dehumidifiers, desiccants.

11. Southwest Desert. Compact configuration and envelope; small ends to east and west; minimal surface exposure; underground is best, with the least exposure to the path of the sun; outside kitchens; decks on top for sleeping; common wall buildings; outside insulation; large thermal mass, thick walls, adobe, earth berms; small windows to east, west, and north can have reflective sills to bounce light to ceiling; sun protection, shading important; all openings should be shaded; use ventilated shading devices; light colors; avoid reflection from neighboring structures and surfaces; can have reflective roof over entire building; shaded outdoor space, especially on north; "ramadas": vernacular example; evaporative cooling with fountains, vegetation; shaded patio or courtyard concept for cooling and ventilation, with rooms opening to inner arcade around court roof; north wall can be designed for radiative cooling at right angles to the clear sky; night sky cooling; roof ponds and radiative mass; cooled water circulate through building mass; night ventilation and flushing of building mass for time-lag cooling.

12. West Texas. Large inner and outer thermal mass to optimize diurnal swings, time-lag cooling; earth-shelter or undergound; built-up roofs; earth berms; good insulation; sun protection via shading, shaded patios, contained patio courtyards, light-colored roofs and walls, shaded east and west elevations; evaporative cooling by landscaping and vegetation, pools, fountains, roof ponds and sprays; spray walls and patios; mechanical evaporative cooling;

natural ventilation; catch prevailing breezes, windows opening to courtyards; water- or air-type heat pumps; radiative cooling.

13. Panhandle, Central Texas, Oklahoma. Natural ventilation, maximum air movement: large, shaded openings, high and low windows, inductive air movement; high ceilings; rooftop air outlets such as belvederes, dormer windows for stack action; night ventilation with thermal mass; capture prevailing breezes; shading, sun protection: porches, trellises, minimal exposure to east and west, shaded outdoor spaces; mass for time-lag cooling: earth-coupling, underground air ducts, earth-to-air heat exchangers, underground construction; evaporative cooling during dry periods; water- or air-type heat pumps; radiative cooling.

14. Bayou Country. High ventilation levels and maximum air movement are needed; cross ventilation; vent roof or attic with belvederes, cupolas, dormer windows; ventilate crawl spaces; elevated living areas; high ceilings; open transoms between rooms; open interior plans; floor-to-ceiling openings with shutters with louvers to control sun and wind; jalousie windows; open siting; inductive ventilation through shafts, stairwells; thermal chimneys; outside living areas to catch prevailing breezes; channel winds with fences, wing walls, vegetation; landscaping not blocking air movement; shading important; ventilated shaded exterior; light-colored roofs and walls; mass can temper diurnal swings; time-lag cooling; underground construction; avoid extra humidity

with dehumidification; design for sun to dry out spaces more than for heating; good drainage.

15. Texas Gulf Coast. Protect from summer sun and heat with shading, external rolling shutters and other external devices; porches; trellises; shaded outdoor living areas; overhangs; second-story balconies; reflective or tinted glass on west and on south if getting glare from water; shade all openings; protect walls from sun; internal zoning to separate heat-producing areas from living spaces; underground construction; natural ventilation: open plans, separated houses; site to catch prevailing breezes; ventilated attic roofs; cross ventilation transoms; large openings; elongated plans; inductive ventilation; avoid extra humidity; effectively ventilate kitchens, baths, laundry; subsurface or drip irrigation instead of spray; permeable paving materials; good drainage; build on high ground.

16. Southern Florida and Hawaii. Full, open ventilation but with louvers or jalousies to control trade wind velocity; single-depth spaces; open plans; hurricane protection; vented attics; outdoor living spaces; avoid overheated microclimate sites; elongated floor plans; inductive ventilation; ceiling-level openings; design to catch directional air flows; good ventilation under house; patio walls or fences to control wind patterns and/or relieve wind pressures; shading and sun protection; light, highly reflective color; reflective roof; shaded outdoor spaces; ventilated shading; interior courts; avoid extra humidity.

Appendix H

Prefabricated, Energy-Core Modules

Joining manufactured with on-site building techniques can create numerous economic and marketing advantages. Home construction financing and labor costs can be particularly reduced by the integration of manufactured, energy-core modules. The modules would contain active and hybrid solar thermal-storage and kitchen, bath, and utility functions. They would substantially reduce the cost of a new home and speed up construction, allowing more rapid market availability and less demand on land-acquisition financing.

Other advantages of this proposed marriage between manufactured and site-built processes, e.g., factory construction and quality control, less dependence on favorable construction weather, and a long-term reduction in utility energy demand, will increase the potential number of home buyers.

The manufacturing of the modules basically involves moving the energy-demanding and energy-intensive elements of home building to indoor, controlled, factory production conditions. These prefabricated energy-core modules proposed by the author would contain a combination of bath with bath, bath with utility, or kitchen with bath, each measuring 8 x 8 x 14 feet (2.4 x 2.4 x 4.3 meters). This is a unit size easily transportable by truck or rail.

Mechanical and electrical distribution would be extendable to serve all specific room requirements. A separate module of equal size would house energy concentrated from solar and internal energies. The energy-storage capability could be for an active solar system with water storage or for a rock-bin or eutectic-salt thermal storage. The energy module would receive waste heat from kitchen appliances and hot water and contain supplemental space heating and domestic water heating equipment, using natural gas, butane, methane, oil, alcohol, kerosene, electricity, or hydrogen (when it is available). The architectural use of these energy modules could be side-by-side, stacked, or segmented (which would be less efficient). Architectural planning would not be very constrained by the integration of these modular energy elements.

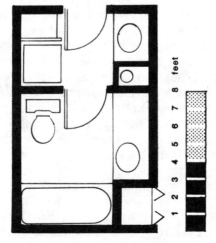

Fig. 183. Energy-core module No. 1

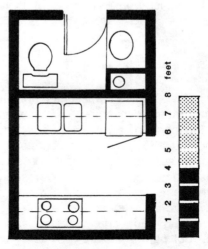

Fig. 184. Energy-core module No. 2

Climatic Profile

A climatic profile determined for the location of your proposed new home is essential for design. Consideration of temperature probability, solar radiation, and proportionate numers of cool or warm days relates to a choice of heating and cooling strategies. Denver, for example, has the following degree-day weather data, insolation, and temperature charts. Similar data for your location can help you in formulating plans and designs that can be appropriate.

Table 9: Degree Days (65F base)

	Average	1979-1980	1980-1981	1981-1982
Nov.	768	941	683	570
Dec.	1,004	939	731	898
Jan.	1,088	1,204	853	1,070
Feb.	902	876	801	918
Mar.	868	828	727	733
Apr.	525	514	260	522

Table 10: Incident Solar Radiation (Btu/sq.ft./day - horizontal surface)

	Average	1979-1980	1980-1981	1981-1982
Nov.	941	812	761	856
Dec.	777	623	555	637
Jan.	895	694	780	727
Feb.	1,208	1,030	898	1,089
Mar.	1,647	1,258	1,366	1,395
Apr.	2,023	1,706	1,727	1,808

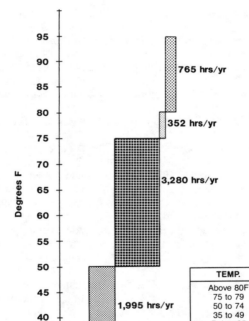

765 hrs/yr
352 hrs/yr
3,280 hrs/yr
1,995 hrs/yr
2,368 hrs/yr

TEMP.	HRS/YR	%
Above 80F	765	8.7
75 to 79	352	4.0
50 to 74	3,280	37.4
35 to 49	1,995	22.8
Below 35	2,368	27.0

Fig. 185: Denver Temperatures for a Typical Year (1964)

References

American Institute of Architects. *Energy in Design: Techniques.* Washington, D.C.: AIA, 1981.

American Society of Heating, Refrigerating, and Air-Conditioning Engineers. *Handbook of Fundamentals.* New York: ASHRAE, 1977.

Anderson, Bruce. *The Solar Home Book: Heating, Cooling, and Designing with the Sun.* Harrisville, N.H.: Cheshire Books, 1976.

Crowther, Richard. *Sun/Earth: Alternative Energy Design for Architecture.* New York: Van Nostrand Reinhold Co., 1983.

Diamond, Stuart. "Energy Products: Don't Get Ripped Off." *New Shelter,* vol. 3, no. 9, Nov.-Dec. 1982, p. 59.

Eccli, Eugene, ed. *Low-Cost Energy-Efficient Shelter for the Owner and Builder.* Emmaus, Pa.: Rodale Press, 1976.

Fisk, Marian Jacobs and Anderson, H.C. William. *Introduction to Solar Technology.* Reading, Mass.: Addison-Wesley Publishing Company, 1982.

Florida Solar Energy Center; *A Handbook for Designing Naturally Ventilated Buildings.* Prepared by Subrato Chandra, Philip W. Fairey, and Robert S. Spain. Cape Canaveral, FL: Florida Solar Energy Center, 1982.

Flower, Bob. "Buying the Right Kind." *New Shelter,* vol. 3, no. 9, Nov.-Dec. 1982, pp. 29-33.

Flower, Bob. "So You Need More?" *New Shelter,* vol. 3, no. 9, Nov.-Dec. 1982, pp. 20-24.

Fuller, Winslow. "Installing Household Heat Exchangers." *Solar Age,* vol. 7, no. 9, Sept. 1982, pp. 22-23.

——. "What's in the Air for Tightly Built Houses?" *Solar Age,* vol. 6, no. 6, June 1981, pp. 30-32.

"Heat Exchangers Effective in Radon Control." *Passive Solar Journal,* vol. 1, no. 1, Jan. 1982, pp. 52-53.

Huber, Hank. "A Step Beyond the Envelope House." *Solar Age,* vol. 7, no. 6, June 1982, p. 24.

IES Lighting Handbook: 1981 Reference Volume. New York: Illuminating Engineering Society of North America, 1981.

Kern, Ken. *The Owner-Built Home.* New York: Charles Scribner's Sons, 1975.

Lafavore, Michael. "Clean Air Indoors." *New Shelter,* vol. 3, no. 5, May-June 1982, pp. 20-27.

Langa, Frederic S. "Enough Is Enough." *New Shelter,* vol. 3, no. 9, Nov.-Dec. 1982, p. 20.

Mazra, Edward. *The Passive-Solar Energy Book: Expanded Professional Edition.* Emmaus, Pa.: Rodale Press, 1979.

National Solar Heating and Cooling Information Center. *Insulation Fact Sheet, DC 101.* Rockville, Md.: NSHCIC, 1977.

Olgyay, Victor. *Design with Climate: Bioclimatic Approach to Architectural Regionalism,* Princeton, NJ: Princeton University Press, 1963.

Orr, Harold and Rob Dumont. "Air Tightness in Buildings." *Alternative Sources of Energy,* no. 53, Jan.-Feb. 1982, pp. 26-27.

"Regional Climate Analysis Design Data: The House Beautiful Climate Control Project." *Bulletin of the American Institute of Architects. Sept. 1949-Jan. 1952.*
Available from: Xerox University Microfilms, 300 North Zeeb Road, Ann Arbor, MI 48106

Ruffner, James A., ed. *Climates of the States.* (2 vols.) 2nd ed. Detroit, Mich.: Gale, 1980.
Available from: Gale Research Company, Book Tower, Detroit, MI 48226

Shurcliff, William A., *Air-to-Air Heat Exchangers for Houses.* Cambridge, Mass.: William A. Shurcliff, 1981.

——. *Superinsulated Houses and Double-Envelope Houses: A Preliminary Survey of Principles and Practices.* Cambridge, Mass.: William A. Shurcliff, 1980.

Stokes, Bruce. "Housing: The Environmental Issues." *Sierra,* vol. 67, no. 5, Sept.-Oct. 1982, p. 45.

Sweet's Catalog File: Products for General Building. New York: McGraw-Hill Book Co., 1982.

Uniform Building Code: 1979 Edition. Prepared by the International Conference of Building Officials. Whittier, Calif.: International Conference of Building Officials, 1979.

United States. Department of Commerce. Environmental Data Earth Science Information Center. *Climatic Atlas of the United States.* Washington, D.C.: U.S. Government Printing Office, 1968. (Reprinted by NOAA, 1974).

Available from: National Climatic Center, Federal Building, Asheville, NC 28801

United States. Department of Energy. *Passive Solar Design Analysis.* Prepared by J. Douglas Balcomb, *Passive Solar Design Handbook,* vol. 2. Springfield, Va.: National Technical Information Service, U.S. Dept. of Commerce, 1980.

United States. Department of Energy. *Passive Solar Design Analysis.* Prepared by J. Douglas Balcomb, et al., *Passive Solar Design Handbook,* vol. 3. Washington, D.C.: U.S. Government Printing Office, 1982.

United States. Department of Housing and Urban Development. *Regional Guidelines for Building Passive Energy Conserving Homes.* Prepared by the American Institute of Architects. Washington, D.C.: U.S. Government Printing Office, 1978.

Wilson, Tom. "How *Not* to Install Insulation." *New Shelter,* vol. 3, no. 9, Nov.-Dec. 1982, pp. 25-28.

Zamm, Alfred V. with Robert Gannon. *Why Your House May Endanger Your Health.* New York: Simon and Schuster, 1980.

Patented Systems

Skytherm North and Skytherm South are thermopond systems invented and patented by Harold Hay. For concept engineering information, write to: Skytherm Processes and Engineering, 2424 Wilshire Boulevard #704, Los Angeles, California 90057.

Glossary

absorptance — the ratio of the radiation absorbed by a surface to the radiation incident on that surface, expressed as a percentage.

active solar system — a solar heating or cooling system that relies on external mechanical power to move the collected heat.

adjustable-rate mortgage (ARM) — a mortgage loan program in which the interest rate is adjusted periodically, usually tied to some kind of index that reflects shifts in short-term credit markets. Also known as a variable-rate mortgage (VRM).

air change — the replacement of a quantity of air in a volume (room or building) within a given period of time, usually expressed in air changes per hour (ACH). The average American home ACH rate is 0.5 to 1.5.

air tempering — heating or cooling incoming, outside air to condition it for use in a ventilation system.

air turbulence — departure in an air stream from a smooth flow, at which the velocity at a given point varies erratically in direction and magnitude.

altitude — the angle of the sun above the horizon calculated in a vertical plane.

azimuth — measurement of the sun's position in plan view (from above), expressed as the distance between true south and the point on the horizon directly below the sun.

bentonite — a soft, porous, expansive clay formed as a weathering product from volcanic ash.

berm — a man-made mound or small hill of earth, often placed against the outer walls of a building to moderate heat gain and heat loss.

biophysics — a branch of knowledge that deals with the application of physical principles and methods to biological problems.

building envelope — the exterior components of construction that enclose interior, conditioned spaces through which thermal energy may be transferred.

cantilever — any structural member or assembly extending from a support at one end but unsupported at the other end.

carcinogen — a cancer-causing agent.

clerestory — a window located in a roof or a wall above the line of vision to provide natural light into a building.

climatic buffer (thermal buffer) — a space or zone in a building, usually in a peripheral location, that intervenes and moderates the impact between the external climate and the interior living space.

cold roof — a type of roof construction with an integral, intervening air space underneath the top roofing surface to prevent ice formation caused by edge melting.

conduction — the transfer of heat energy between two bodies that are in direct contact by the motion of adjacent atoms and molecules.

convection — heat transfer by movement of a fluid (liquid, gas, or vapor) between the fluid and a surface or within the fluid itself.

convective air movement (natural convection) — a circulation of air caused by differences in density resulting from temperature changes.

covenant — in real estate, a clause containing a subordinate agreement or stipulation, primarily in a deed, often specifying an architectural and/or land use restriction.

daylighting — the use of natural light for illumination through toplighting, sidelighting, and/or uplighting (reflection).

degree day, heating — a unit used to estimate the heating-fuel consumption and the nominal heating load (demand) of a building. For any one day, when the mean temperature is less than 65 F, there exists as many degree days as there are Fahrenheit degrees difference in temperature between the mean temperature for the day and 65 F. The sum of the degree days constitutes the annual degree day heating requirements.

dehumidification — the condensation of water vapor from air by cooling below the dewpoint or removal of water vapor from air by chemical or physical methods.

destratification — in this case, the relocation by mechanical means of the upper, warm air strata in a building for more effective use.

direct gain — solar radiation directly intercepting or entering a building. In a direct gain passive solar system, sunlight enters south, east, or west glazed openings, and is absorbed by thermal mass, converted to heat and/or reflected to other interior surfaces.

drain back — a liquid-type, active solar collection system in which the fluid in the collector loop drains to some type of containment during freezing conditions or power outages, protecting the collectors from damage caused by freezing. The collector fluid is pumped back into the system.

drain down — a liquid-type, active solar collection system similar to a drain-back system, except that the collector fluid is not recovered when it drains.

easement — a privilege, right, or interest in land owned by another that entitles its holder to a specific limited use or enjoyment, such as right of way or access to utilities.

emissivity — the capacity of a material to emit radiant energy.

emittance — a ratio of the amount of energy radiated by a surface to that of a blackbody (a perfect absorber of heat that emits none) at the same temperature.

envelope — an additional, thermal shell around the architecture that protects from heat losses or gains and acts as a thermal intervenor.

equinox — either of two times each year when the sun crosses the equator and the length of day and night are approximately equal, being on or about March 22 and September 22.

equity — the money value of a property or of an interest in a property in excess of claims or liens against it.

eutectic salts (phase-change materials) — a combination of two (or more) mutually soluble materials that are used for heat storage. These materials melt at low temperatures, absorbing large quantities of heat through phase change from a solid to a liquid. Heat is released when reverse phase change occurs as the materials cool.

evapotranspiration — loss of water from the soil by both evaporation and by transpiration from plants growing in the soil.

exfiltration — indoor air leakage to the exterior through the building envelope caused by a pressure differential.

fenestration — the series or arrangement of windows in a building; a term used to signify an opening in a building to admit light and/or air.

glazing — a .covering of transparent or translucent material (glass or plastic) used for admitting light.

heat exhanger — a device used to transfer heat between two physically separate fluids.

holistic — of or relating to holism, a viewpoint that the universe and especially living nature is correctly seen in terms of interacting wholes that are more than the mere sum of elementary particles.

hybrid solar system — a passive solar system requiring mechanical assistance for energy distribution.

hydronic — referring to a heating system that transfers heat by means of a fluid contained in a closed system of pipes.

inductive ventilation — natural ventilation enhanced and induced through a rising air column generated by temperature differentials. If warm air is vented at a high exhaust outlet, cooler air from a low-level intake will flow into the space, replacing the warm air. This "stack effect" or "chimney effect" depends upon the temperature differential, the height between the inlet and outlet, and the size of the apertures.

infiltration — the uncontrolled movement of outdoor air into the interior of a building through cracks around doors and windows or in walls, roofs, and floors.

insolation — the amount of solar radiation — direct, diffused, and reflected — striking a surface during a specified period of time at a given orientation. From **In**cident **Sol**ar Radi**ation**.

invert — the depth factor from the grade line to the water-flow depth in a sewer.

ion — an electrically charged atom or group of atoms caused by gain or loss of one or more electrons.

life-cycle costing (life-cycle cost analysis) — the total cost of a system over its economically useful life. Includes the appropriate summation of all the costs expected to be incurred as a result of choosing and implementing any particular plan and design over the life of the building.

macroclimate — the overall climatic conditions in a given region.

mat (matt, matte) — a dead or dull finish free from shine or highlights; or a roughened, granular surface.

microclimate — the climate at a specific site as defined by local variations on the regional climate caused by topography, vegetation, soils, water conditions, as well as man-made construction.

natural ventilation — supplying and removing air by natural means (such as by wind or natural convection) to or from any space.

negative ionization — introducing negative ions into a space, often for air cleaning purposes.

opaque — impenetrable by light.

outgassing — emission of gases and/or respirable particles; usually referring to emission of toxic contaminants from unstable synthetic materials, maintenance products, and finishes used in indoor environments.

passive solar system — a solar heating or cooling system that uses no external mechanical power to move the collected solar heat.

photovoltaic — referring to a semiconductor that converts solar energy into electricity (direct current).

plenum — a compartment for the passage and distribution of air.

psychoneural — relating to or affecting the mind and nervous system.

radiation — transmission of heat by electromagnetic waves through space; the passage of heat from one object to another without warming the space between.

radiative cooling — the cooling of a building or heat storage device by the radiation of excess heat, usually to the clear sky.

radon — a radioactive gas formed by the disintegration of radium in soils. Certain building materials such as brick, stone, plaster, sand and gravel may also contain radon, as can well water.

radon "daughters" — radon gas decay products formed by the disintegration of radon nuclei.

reflectance — the ratio of the amount of radiation reflected by a surface to the amount of radiation incident on the surface.

regenerative — of, relating to, or marked by renewal and revitalization.

R-value (R-factor) — the measure of a material's resistance to heat flow. The higher the R-value, the greater the resistance.

selective filtration — choosing appropriate filter media to meet specific needs.

setback — a zoning restriction on use within a given distance from the property line.

sky vault (skydome) — the visible hemisphere of sky, above the horizon, in all directions.

slip joint — a construction means that allows for differential movement between materials.

solar chimney — a solar-heated plenum used for inductive air movement, placed on the west or south exposure of a building. Can be used for inductive solar cooling.

solar pond — a shallow body of water used to collect solar energy, usually lined with black plastic to increase absorption. High concentrations of salt are often added to the pond to create a high-density, high-temperature layer near the bottom of the pond that reduces convective energy losses.

specular — mirror-like.

stratification — the tendency of heated air (or other fluid) to rise and arrange itself in layers, the top layer being warmer than the bottom.

thermal break — an element of low heat conductivity placed in such a way as to reduce or prevent the flow of heat.

thermal bridging — conductive heat loss or gain through building members and materials.

thermal mass — a substance (liquid or solid) in which heat energy is stored. Also, the amount of potential heat storage capacity available in a given assembly or system.

thermosiphoning — the convective circulation of a fluid that occurs in a closed system when less dense, warm fluid rises and is displaced by denser, cooler fluid in the same system.

topography — the configuration of a surface including its relief and the position of its natural and man-made features.

translucent — the quality of transmitting light but causing sufficient diffusion to eliminate perception of distinct images.

transmissivity — the capacity of a material to transmit radiant energy.

transmittance — the ratio of radiant energy transmitted through a substance to the total radiant energy incident on its surface.

transparent — the quality of transmitting light so that objects or images can be seen as if there were no intervening material.

U-value (coefficient of heat transmission) — the heat flow rate through a given construction assembly, air to air, expressed in Btu/hr/sq. ft./degree Fahrenheit difference between indoor and outdoor temperatures. The reciprocal of R-value.

vapor barrier — a component of construction that is impervious to the flow of moisture, used to prevent moisture travel to a point where it may condense.

variable-rate mortgage (VRM) — see adjustable-rate mortgage.

vasoconstriction — narrowing of the blood vessels.

visual accommodation — the eye's ability to bring images at various distances into sharp focus or to shift focus from one object to another at a different distance.

zero-property line — a zoning right to build structures to a property line.

NOTICE

Construction drawings are available based upon the conceptual plans in this book. Any set of drawings may be modified to fit the local climate and other conditions at your site. Contact Solarchitecture, 3201 East 3rd Avenue, Denver, Colorado 80206; area code 303 355-2302.